About the Author

Kader Abdolah (1954, Iran) is t[illegible] Dutch novels released in English translation: *My Father's Notebook* (2004), *The House of the Mosque* (2010), and *The King* (2014).

Having arrived in the Netherlands in 1988 as a political refugee, his efforts to learn the language paid off. He started writing in Dutch and in 1995 was the recipient of an incentive grant for promising new authors. He went on to write many award-winning novels. *The Messenger* and *The Qur'an* (2008), originally published in Dutch as a two-book set, have been received in the Netherlands with high regard.

Additionally, the author has been honoured with many distinctions including the Mundial Award for his achievements in the area of international cooperation, peace, and security, and the Order of Orange-Nassau in recognition of his contributions to society and the world of literature. Abdolah's writing talent has not gone unnoticed; his work has already been translated into thirty languages.

About the Translators

Nouri and Niusha Nighting met when they were graduate students abroad. While travelling in the Middle East in that period, they experienced the Hajj firsthand. This later inspired them to explore Islamic culture and literature. They have translated many related academic essays and books, but have always been keen to tackle more literary work. Kader Abdolah's *The Qur'an* and *The Messenger* are their first collaborative efforts.

MIX
Papier van
verantwoorde herkomst
FSC® C004472

Kader Abdolah

The Messenger

A Tale Retold

Translated from the Dutch by
Niusha and Nouri Nighting

World Editions

Published in Great Britain in 2016 by World Editions Ltd., London

www.worldeditions.org

First published as *De boodschapper* in the Netherlands in 2008 by De Geus BV, PO Box 1878, 4801 BW Breda

British Library Cataloguing-in-Publication Data
A catalogue record for this book is available on request from the British Library.

ISBN 978-94-6238-015-8

Typeset in Minion Pro

The publisher gratefully acknowledges the support of the Dutch Literary Foundation.

Nederlands letterenfonds
dutch foundation for literature

Distribution Europe (except the Netherlands and Belgium): Turnaround Publisher Services, London
Distribution the Netherlands and Belgium: Centraal Boekhuis, Culemborg, the Netherlands

Phone: +31 (0)76 523 3533. Email: info@worldeditions.org

This book is dedicated to Zayd ibn Harithah and Zayd ibn Thabit

While the stories and events in *The Messenger* are based on historical fact, everything here may well be read according to the conventions of fiction.

KADER ABDOLAH

For the reader's benefit:
Names from the Qur'an
with their Biblical counterparts

Dawud	David
Hajar	Hagar
Ibrahim	Abraham
Isa	Jesus
Isma'il	Ishmael
Jabra'il	Gabriel
Maryam	Mary
Musa	Moses
Nuh	Noah
Sulayman	Solomon

1 Zayd, the Chronicler

Kindly let me introduce myself, my name is Zayd ibn Thalith.

I was the chronicler of the messenger Muhammad, his personal scribe.

The messenger did not have a son of his own. He adopted me when I was about seven years old.

Everyone called me Zayd ibn Muhammad—Zayd, the son of Muhammad.

I must have been five years old when my mother took me to visit family in the city of Ta'if.

I do not actually remember anything about that trip, but many years later my mother told me about the journey, 'We rode through the desert in a caravan of twelve camels. I always had you on my lap. High up on the saddle, you sat still and took in the surroundings, but whenever the caravan stopped to rest, I had difficulty keeping you with me. You ran in every direction and went off with anybody who asked. At the marketplace in Ta'if, you pulled your hand loose from mine and disappeared behind a stand. I ran after you but couldn't find you. I looked behind other stands—no Zayd. I cried, shouted for you, ran back and forth, but you were nowhere to be found. When the market day ended, and everybody had gone, I was left there … alone and empty handed. I didn't dare go home to your father. I had lost his favourite son.'

Thus you understand that I, Zayd, was stolen, but I am not sure how it happened. I cannot remember my mother or that marketplace either. But I do have a clear image of myself exposed and dirty, squatting in a cage with other naked boys like a pack of monkeys.

I later heard I was sold from one person to another for two years.

When I was seven years old, a small-time slave owner from Mecca purchased me at the market in Jandal and took me home with him.

This merchant's name was Hakim ibn Hizam. His belly was big and round.

From that moment on, I can remember almost everything; it was a turning point in my life.

I knew I originally came from Mecca, and I kept hoping I would run into my parents on the street or at the slave market. I recited their names under my breath the entire day, lest I forget them.

My father's name was Sabit bin Sharasil.

My mother's name was Sadi bint Salab.

I dreamt of the moment I would see my mother at the marketplace and shout, 'Sadi bint Salab, it's me, your son Zayd!'

Though the mother and father I had imagined would not be the same in reality. Besides, they would never recognize me. I had changed so much. The sun had baked my skin a deep shade of brown.

Yet, nothing is as unpredictable as fate.

The slave owner Hakim ibn Hizam took me home and let me loose in his courtyard, much like you would a wild goat. Shortly afterwards, I was allowed to set foot in the house.

On the very first day, I heard a loud knocking, and my master shouted, 'Zayd, open the door!'

Of course, I did what was asked of me. An older woman came inside. I thought she was my master's wife.

'What do we have here?' she kindly said.

I stared at her in silence.

Then she asked, 'What's your name?'

'His name is Zayd,' my master shouted from his workroom, 'I bought him at the market in Jandal.'

The woman was my master's aunt. They talked for a while, and when she came out of his office she said, 'Come along, you're going with me.'

I looked at my master questioningly. 'You're in luck, Zayd. My aunt doesn't have a son, and she just bought you. She's your new owner now. Her name is Khadija. Be a good boy.'

Khadija grabbed my hand, and we went on our way.

Although I was only a child, I immediately sensed I had ended up somewhere wonderful. In comparison to other houses in Mecca, Khadija lived in a small palace. She had me wash and change my clothes. I became a person again, a normal boy.

As evening approached, her husband arrived home.

'Look! I have a surprise for you,' she said, pointing at me smiling.

Her husband's name was Muhammad ibn Abdullah. Many years later, he would become the messenger of Allah.

The next morning Muhammad shouted, 'Zayd, time to go!'

He was my new master. So of course I did not ask where we were going. I just followed along behind him.

I had no idea he was intent on finding my parents.

And, as fate would have it, he actually found them. They could not believe their eyes. Was I really their son? So tall, so well groomed, dressed in such fine clothing. My mother was clutching the wall for support, speechless from the shock. My father dropped to the floor at Muhammad's feet to thank him, but Muhammad graciously helped him up.

I spent a week in my father's small, ramshackle house, but on Friday he brought me back to Muhammad and said, 'His destiny is in your hands. If he's happy, we're happy.'

That is how I became Muhammad's son.

Khadija was Muhammad's first wife.

She taught me to read and write, but Muhammad was my master. I shadowed his every move, until the day he died.

All those years, I never thought about why I stayed with him.

In hindsight, however, I do understand. I had a passion for poetry, and I could completely lose myself in the tales Muhammad told.

When he began his mission as the messenger, my life completely changed as well. Unless he sent me off somewhere, I never left his side.

Whenever a text was revealed to him, he shuddered uncontrollably, dropped to his knees, knelt pressing his head to the ground like a horse, and uttered incoherent words.

We were usually alone when this happened, and of course it was frightening the first few times. I did not know what to do, so I rushed off to get Khadija.

As time passed, I did this less and less. I realized it was my task to stay by Muhammad's side. I needed to work out how best to handle the situation.

I would patiently wait as he received a revelation, until he collapsed on the ground, exhausted. Then I quickly covered him with a blanket and let him rest.

By the time Muhammad died, I was a grown man. My hair was black, but my moustache was already streaked with grey.

I was still deep in mourning when a rider on a brown Arabian horse stopped at my gate.

'Zayd,' the man cried. Umar had sent his courier.

I did not hesitate. I knew why I was being summoned. I mounted my horse and went with him.

After Muhammad, Umar was the most important leader of Islam. When Muhammad died, Umar was the one who took over the reins. He was also a shrewd leader and a ruthless warlord.

I knelt before him in a cold sweat.

'Zayd ibn Thalith!' Umar exclaimed, 'Muhammad is gone, yet we don't have his revelations. Gather up his texts. Now! It's a matter of urgency.'

I knew Umar well, he knew me, no other words were necessary.

I kissed the back of his hand, went outside, jumped on my horse, and rushed out of town into the countryside. I was so overjoyed with the task bestowed upon me, I had trouble finding my way home.

That night I could not sleep. Oh, what a splendid night, what a magnificent undertaking! How best to proceed now? I had witnessed the revelation of some of his texts myself. However, I would have to rely on the memory of his followers for the rest.

I went over to the open window and gazed at the boundless, clear night sky above the desert.

I, Zayd ibn Thalith, would be the one to commit the words of the Qur'an to writing.

A man who receives such an honour must fight back tears not to die of happiness.

As soon as the first rays of light struck my window, I packed my bags and saddled my horse.

And I set out to fulfil my glorious task!

2 In Search of the Qur'an

First, I visited Muhammad's wives. They kindly gave me verses that had been written down long ago, embroidered on their nightgowns, and engraved in precious gold coins.

'Is there nothing more?' I asked.

Aisha, the beautiful, young, redheaded widow of Muhammad unlatched a gold pendant and handed it to me. Finely engraved on the back were the words:

'He holds up the stars lest they fall to the ground …'

I then travelled day and night looking for other texts in all corners of the realm.

I listened and noted down everything I came across.

After seven months, I returned with three camels weighed down with parchments inscribed with Qur'an texts, broad camel bones and pieces of wood carved with verses, and cloth colourfully embroidered with the words of the Qur'an.

Back home, I went into my room and shut the door behind me. I did not set foot outside for a year, until I had completed the Qur'an.

When I had finished, the sun shone in my heart. I put on clean clothing and my best leather shoes. I tucked the brand new Book under my arm and rode like a prince to Umar's house.

I knelt before him and proudly said, 'The Qur'an!'

I had accomplished my task.

3 Umar, the Second Successor to Muhammad

However, it was not that simple.

Those who objected to my Qur'an voiced their opinions. They represented six powerful Islamic movements, each with a different interpretation of Muhammad's teachings. They claimed I had written my own Qur'an, which had nothing to do with Muhammad's original tellings.

It was not my place to speak on the matter. It was Umar's decision.

Unity was necessary in those days.

Umar decided that the Qur'an I had compiled would not be made public but would be kept within the circles of power as a foundation—as a source of inspiration.

Later, when Umar was killed and Uthman succeeded him, the discussion about this Qur'an flared up again.

Early one morning, representatives of the six powerful Islamic movements appeared at Uthman's gate. Their camels were loaded down with writings.

Uthman had the camels led into the walled courtyard. Then the gate was locked behind them.

The camels were unloaded and the writings stacked in piles. 'Zayd, go through it all, add what's necessary and remove what's unnecessary. Take all the time you need!' said Uthman. And off he went.

I was busy with these excerpts and texts for the longest time. On a few occasions, I visited experts to consult with them. Finally the day arrived when I could let Uthman know the work was done. Uthman came to me. A carpet was rolled out in the courtyard, and a lantern was fetched.

Uthman ordered everybody out of the house.

I took a seat behind a low writing table, opened my Qur'an and handed Uthman a list of remarks related to points I was still doubting about.

He took a seat and attentively went through my list. Then he came and sat beside me on the carpet. He dictated a few sentences and indicated with his finger where I needed to add these to the Book. And I followed his instructions.

It was a long night of thinking; I was drenched in sweat.

Then I suddenly got the most wonderful idea. I had written down the texts one after the other, in no particular order. It occurred to me that the texts would be clearer if I divided them into one hundred and fourteen parts: the Qur'an in one hundred and fourteen suras, or chapters. And what if I gave each chapter a title? 'The Table'; 'The Bees'; 'The Four Feet'; 'The Women'; 'Maryam' and so on—that would make it even clearer.

However, something was still missing, but what? Again, I had an inspiration; something magical happened. I discovered a non-existent letter, a character without any meaning—an insignificant mark, a dot, a small star.

I placed that dot, or that small star at the end of every sentence. It was unbelievable. Somehow, those insignificant marks conveyed so much. They created clarity, insight, and joy. I then added one hundred and fourteen titles and thousands of small stars to the text.

The Qur'an is from Allah.

The order, the titles, the stars and dots in the Qur'an are my doing, are from Zayd—the chronicler, the scribe.

With the new Qur'an in his hand, light-headed with happiness, Uthman extinguished the lantern and said, 'Zayd! We're done! Destroy the rest.'

'Destroy?' I asked him.

'Burn everything!' he ordered.

At dawn the next day, Uthman appeared in the courtyard to inspect the smouldering ashes.

Seven horsemen carried the Qur'an—veiled in sheer green fabric—to the mosque. They gently placed the Book on a pedestal.

Uthman drew his sword and laid it on the Book: 'Here you have the Qur'an!'

No one dared utter a word.

Everyone could now pay homage to the Book.

4 The Life of Muhammad

When I started gathering up the texts of the Qur'an, I realized something important: you cannot understand the Qur'an without having a good understanding of Muhammad.

I myself discovered a new Muhammad while working on the Book.

I originally saw him as a dreamer, as a man who truly enjoyed life—with a passion for women—and as a leader who took incredible risks.

Yet, once I started transcribing his words, I saw him as a person, an inquiring individual. Before that, I had always regarded him as a father, my master, a warlord, and a prophet. Muhammad the man was my discovery and that is what I wanted to share with the world.

I knew that later on people would add a lot to his life story, and perhaps others would leave out a lot. So I said to myself, 'Zayd! Set down Muhammad's life in writing.'

In Umar's day—when he had kept the Qur'an I compiled from the public—I had packed my bags, mounted my horse, and set out again, but this time to collect untold stories about Muhammad's life. And I had expected this momentous task to take me until the end of my days.

To find out more about Muhammad's younger years, I had to return to the Mecca of the past—to the place where he was born.

Allow me to tell you something about the practices and circumstances of the Mecca of his youth. Particularly about the Kaaba, where the idols were kept.

In fact, Muhammad's life was characterized by a single dream. He wanted to smash the idols and purify the Kaaba, to bestow it on Allah as a sanctuary.

Therefore, if I am going to talk about Muhammad, I should probably begin with the Kaaba and its idols. Or perhaps even better, with the city of Mecca.

5 Mecca

Mecca was a centre of trade. Three hundred and sixty-five idols were kept in the Kaaba. These graven images were made of stone and wood, decorated with fabric, and painted in gold and joyful colours.

There were also a few large effigies on the Kaaba Square.

The Persian Empire was our eastern neighbour. The Persians had already been monotheistic for a few thousand years; they had one God called Ahura Mazda. Zarathustra was their prophet, and their sacred Book was called the *Avesta.*

The Byzantine Empire was our western neighbour. The Byzantines were also monotheistic; they had one God and one prophet, who was called Isa or Jesus. They also had a sacred Book: the *Injil* or *Gospel of Isa.*

The population of Mecca consisted of many clans and tribes, and each had their own idols. All these idols had been given a place in the cube-shaped building known as the Kaaba.

Nobody really knows who made the Kaaba. It is an ancient structure that has always served as a place of worship.

We do know that the ancient prophet Ibrahim once placed a large, mysterious black stone in a wall of the Kaaba. We believe this stone fell from the heavens and that Isma'il, the prophet Ibrahim's son, found it.

Ibrahim used this divine rock as a cornerstone for the Kaaba. We call it *al-Hajar al-Aswad*, the Black Stone.

We do not know much more about the history of the Kaaba, although some people believe Ibrahim was also the maker of the Kaaba.

We were desert dwellers, a people who lagged behind civilized nations that had one God and one Book. That is why Muhammad wanted to clear out the idols and give the Kaaba to one God, a God who inhabited the Seventh Level of Heaven. The God of Muhammad called Allah, which means: He is One.

It was always very busy on the Kaaba Square on Fridays. People then came to offer sacrifices to their idols.

Muhammad refused to show his face there. But one night, when I was still a child, I went to the Kaaba on my own. I secretly peered inside from behind a thick black curtain. In the semi-darkness, the damp, warm air filled with sweet scents engulfed me. Candles burned in large holders, their light reflecting in the gold and silver. The flickering light and shadows made the idols look big and scary. People bowed down to lay their offerings at the feet of the statues. This was forbidden territory for a child, yet I slipped through the curtain into the room. In the darkness, I crept along the idols, touching their glittering garments and golden swords. Then, an old man caught me in the act. He grabbed me by the ear and sent me on my way.

6 The Distribution of Power in Mecca

At that time in Mecca, the hierarchy of power was as follows:

- Idols
- Slave owners
- Wealthy merchants
- Jews
- Camels
- Men
- Male slaves
- Female slaves
- Goats
- Women

The slave owners put their slaves to work on farms and in the desert. And they sold the children of their slaves to the merchants.

The camel was the symbol of prosperity. The more camels someone had, the more wealth and power he possessed. The wealthy merchants sometimes had hundreds of camels and countless numbers of people working for them. Their caravans were loaded with goods brought from the Byzantine Empire, which were then transported to the eastern borders to be exchanged with the wares of Persian merchants.

The Jews traded textiles and gold. Besides their trading activities, they earned piles of dirty money charging interest on loans. Moreover, the Jews behaved arrogantly because they had a Holy Book. They felt superior and looked down on others.

Women were treated like animals. Every wealthy man had twenty, sometimes as many as thirty wives at home. They also owned countless numbers of female slaves, and when they were away from home, they took pleasure in the company of loose women.

The female slaves had more power than ordinary women had, because they worked hard and were indispensable as farm labour.

The men felt disgraced every time their wives gave birth to a daughter. Those who already had many daughters sacrificed their newborn girls to their idols.

These were the practices when Muhammad was born. His father's name was Abdullah. He died shortly before Muhammad's birth.

His mother's name was Amina. Because she could not breastfeed him, another woman nursed him. When Muhammad was five, his mother died.

His grandfather became his guardian. He died when Muhammad was nine years old, and his eldest uncle took custody of him. Muhammad called him Uncle Talib. Uncle Talib sent Muhammad into the mountains with a herd of goats to earn his keep. Thus, Muhammad became a shepherd.

7 Jahiz, Mecca's Oldest Market Trader

Uncle Talib, Muhammad's guardian, was a small-time trader. He had a stand at Mecca's Friday market. Once Muhammad was older, he no longer had to watch over the goats. Instead, Uncle Talib put Muhammad to work as a runner.

To find out more about those days, I went to see Jahiz bin Ismail, the oldest trader on Mecca's market. Over the years, he had lost his eyesight. I put this question to him, 'Jahiz, you've spent your entire life here. You saw Muhammad working on the market as a boy. Is there something more you can tell me about him? What was he like, back then, what kinds of goods did he sell?'

'What can I say about him? It was so long ago,' Jahiz replied. 'Muhammad was a shy boy with long, black hair and dark-brown eyes. He quietly stood behind the stall the entire day. If I remember correctly, he sold goods like goat cheese, camel fat, bowls of honey, bunches of dates, bottles of olive oil, dried figs, broad camel bones with iron pins used for writing, sprigs of dried mint, bottled rose water in boxes. And stone statues of idols.

'Young Muhammad kept a watchful eye over everything.

'I remember an incident involving an old Jewish merchant next to my stall. He didn't have a stall of his own but sat on the ground. He sold gold and silver rings and all his customers were women. He actually had a money trade. He provided loans to these women, and they gave him their rings, bracelets, and necklaces as security.

"Jahiz!" Muhammad called to me.

‘It was busy on the market, I had trouble hearing him.

“Jahiz!” he cried again.

“What did you say Muhammad?” I shouted over the crowd.

“That woman,” he replied while pointing to the Jewish merchant.

‘I looked, but nothing unusual struck me.

“Uncle Talib,” Muhammad then called to his uncle, who was talking to some merchants a few stands further.

“What is it?” his uncle asked.

‘Muhammad pointed at the Jewish merchant again. However, his uncle saw nothing unusual either.

“Qasim!” Muhammad cried to a merchant further down.

‘In the meantime, I came out from behind my stall to see what was going on. I saw a woman holding the Jewish merchant’s hand and pleading, “In the name of your prophet Musa. Give me back my ring.”

‘But the man wouldn’t hear of it because the woman hadn’t paid the interest on her loan in time.

‘Suddenly Talib and Qasim also appeared. The three of us hovered over the Jewish merchant, and he was obliged to return the woman’s gold ring—all due to Muhammad’s attentiveness.’

‘Jahiz, do you remember anything else about him from that period?’ I asked.

‘At the marketplace, the poets placed a stool on a busy spot,’ Jahiz related, ‘then they would stand on it to recite their poems. People always gathered around a poet to listen. If they liked a poem, they threw coins. People liked the work of the desert poets best. Their poems told tales of sand; horses; the moon; the sword; snakes; fire; wine, and the ravishingly beautiful, untamed women of the desert. The best poem of the year was written on a large piece of parchment and hung on the left wall of the Kaaba.

'Muhammad was captivated by these poets; fascinated by poetry.'

What Jahiz told me was consistent with a story I had heard about Muhammad as a youngster from Ibrahim bin Zahiri, a hide trader. This Ibrahim had in turn heard it from his father. It went something like this, 'The desert poet Abu Rahman recited his new poem. Oh, what a poem! Everyone admired him; everyone threw coins. In a state of rapture, Muhammad removed his new camel-skin coat and tossed it to the poet, as a reward for his eloquent poem.'

8 Sabir, the Scrap Metal Merchant

I had searched far and wide for people who might tell me more about Muhammad in his younger years, but I could not find anybody else.

So when Jahiz mentioned a merchant named Qasim, I got very excited, 'Jahiz, who was this Qasim, what did he sell, where does he live? Is he even still alive?'

'Qasim is long dead. He traded metal. He had seven sons and no daughters. That's why he strolled around the market as proud as a camel with a long neck. Go talk to his eldest son. If I remember correctly, he was the same age as Muhammad.'

'Where can I find Qasim's son? Do you know his name?'

'I've never been very good with names. Sometimes I even forget my own name,' Jahiz said. 'I think his seven sons are still in the metal trade. Go to the bazaar in Mecca or to the bazaar in Ta'if. Mention the name of Qasim and the number seven; you are certain to find one of his sons.'

I took his advice, and with success.

Qasim's eldest son was called Sabir. He had a large piece of property on the Ta'if Bazaar and indeed traded metal. His hair was completely grey, but his posture was straight as an arrow.

He received me in the courtyard of his shop, on a bench in the shade of an old olive tree, and had sweetened rose water brought for me.

I am not sure what he expected from my visit but certainly not that I would ask him all about Muhammad, about the distant past when he worked on the market as a boy.

‘Now, there’s a question,’ he said, smiling, as he removed his pipe from his pocket. ‘It’s quite a long time ago. What exactly do you want to know?’

‘Do you have any memories of Muhammad? Something that has stayed with you since that time?’

‘He was different from us,’ Sabir said, and he lit his pipe, ‘we were a ragged bunch of street children; he came from a prominent clan. His grandfather was the keyholder of the Kaaba. Nobody on the market knew me, but all the merchants knew Muhammad. I’m not sure what I can possibly tell you that you don’t already know. I do remember that Muhammad knew many poems by heart.

‘When it was quiet on the market and the merchants gathered together to smoke a water pipe, they’d call on him, “Muhammad, recite a poem!” And though he hardly spoke otherwise, he’d immediately recite something.’

‘Do you remember any of the poems?’

He laughed, ‘What a question. Me? A poem? No. Though I think Muhammad knew all of the poems those market poets recited by heart.’

‘And who were those poets?’

‘I don’t know. I’m not a man of poetry. Nor of poets.’

Given Sabir could not remember the name of even one poet from that time, I went in search of poems by the desert poet Abu Rahman. I discovered the most beautiful love poem:

‘Jamila!
The tawny desert snakes recoil
The deadly scorpions are struck helpless
And the olive trees drop their black fruit

Whenever you, in your pomegranate-coloured dress,
wander past my house
Barefoot in the hot sand.'

9 Bahira, the Holy Monk

When I asked around about Muhammad's childhood, people often mentioned a meeting between the young Muhammad and an old monk named Bahira.

It is basically a story Muhammad's followers once told, which has been exaggerated over time.

But Muhammad's enemies and the Jews in particular said it was a lie, a fantasy designed to place Muhammad among the old prophets Isa, Musa, and Ibrahim.

The Jews could have been right; the story might have been fabricated, but the monk Bahira and his monastery were not made up.

In search of that monastery, I left Mecca early in the morning and rode toward the Red Sea until sundown.

On the way, I stumbled upon an old caravanserai beside a large crossroads, where traders from other cities would stop to rest their camels and sell their wares.

I spent a comfortable night there, in the inn.

Further along, at the foot of the mountains, stood the monastery where Bahira had once lived.

The Christian merchants, who spent the night in this caravanserai in earlier days, always visited the monastery the next day to express their admiration for Bahira. They gathered in front of the monastery door and waited until the monk came outside for a moment.

In the caravanserai, the merchants told me that Bahira spent almost his entire life in the monastery; he did not leave it until the day he died. They considered him a saint, someone who had original parchment writings of the ancient prophets Ibrahim, Musa, and Isa in a closet in his library. They believed he possessed knowledge of age-old secrets.

Bahira was long dead, and I was now staying in that very same caravanserai. At night, I went for a short walk outside. I could see the flickering lights of the monastery in the distance.

At dawn the next day, I rode there. Since Bahira's death, hardly anyone visited the monastery anymore. From far away, it looked deserted.

I tied up my horse and entered the building.

'Is anybody here?' I called a few times, but there was no response.

I continued further.

A nun appeared. I understood that only nuns lived here now and that this nun ran the monastery. Her name was Hajar, and she was already quite old.

She thought I was a Christian merchant who had come to make a donation, so she greeted me respectfully and escorted me to her office. I placed a bag of silver coins on her desk, sat down on a bench and said, 'Sister Hajar, I'm actually here for another reason. I'm busy gathering information about Muhammad's life. There's a story that as a boy of ten or twelve he met the monk Bahira. Some say it's true. Others insist it was made up to glorify Muhammad. Perhaps you remember something about that meeting?'

The nun put the bag of coins in her desk drawer and wearily said, 'Muhammad, Muhammad. Why is it always about

Muhammad? Quite frankly, we don't know what to think of him. Fortunately, we live at the foot of the mountains with our backs to Mecca so we are spared the nonsense there. If the young Muhammad ever visited our monastery, certainly I didn't experience this personally. I was a child at the time. However, there is no doubt that he met Bahira. Nobody knows how this boy ended up travelling with the Christian merchants.

'Whenever Bahira went outside, a crowd of people always gathered around him to touch his golden staff. One day, amongst the merchants, Bahira saw a boy with black curly hair who didn't look like a Christian.

"What's your name, child?" Bahira had asked.

"Muhammad."

"Which tribe are you from?"

"Quraysh."

"And your father's name?"

"Abdullah."

"Who did you come with?"

"With my uncle."

"What's your uncle's name?"

"Talib."

'The monk paused for a moment, then leaned forward to whisper something in Muhammad's ear.'

'What might that have been?' I asked.

'We never found out,' she said, 'but here in the monastery they say Bahira later remarked, "That child had an unusual quality about him."'

The rest of the story comes from a version the Arabs tell.

Bahira escorted Muhammad inside and invited Uncle Talib to join them. The monk then took Talib aside, talked with him privately, and started leafing through some ancient, secret writings.

No, the monk was not mistaken. Muhammad was the individual whose coming had been foretold. It was clearly stated in one of the secret writings that it would be a boy with the sign of a moon on his left shoulder.

With trembling hands the priest and Uncle Talib lifted Muhammad's shirt and indeed, to their amazement, they saw a crescent moon on his shoulder.

Bahira blessed Muhammad with his golden cross and whispered in his ear, 'Take care of yourself.'

This was more than enough proof for the Arabs that Muhammad was the successor to Isa and that he belonged among the prophets Sulayman, Dawud, Musa, and Ibrahim.

10 The Merchant Waraqa Discovers Muhammad

Until he was fifteen, Muhammad worked for Uncle Talib—who fully entrusted his regular stand on the market to him—while each day Talib took his wares by camel along to marketplaces in the surrounding villages.

Later, when Muhammad had outgrown his uncle's stand, he went to work for some of the bigger traders. He was seventeen when the merchant Waraqa discovered him.

Waraqa had a large storehouse where he sold agricultural equipment to merchants: iron ploughs, shovels, pickaxes, nails, ropes, and stone for construction. There was always new equipment being put on display.

Waraqa was looking for a skilled helper. His brother-in-law, who worked on the market too, told him about Muhammad, 'He works hard and he's reliable.'

Waraqa employed Muhammad but quickly realized that Muhammad was not meant to be a shopkeeper for very long; he was an unusual youngster.

I, Zayd, had known Waraqa since my childhood. I shall return to that later.

11 In Search of Waraqa

I found Waraqa in the courtyard of his large house in the centre of Mecca. He was sitting on the ground by the fountain, playing with his grandchildren in the shade of an old date palm. I had approached his son beforehand, so Waraqa knew I was coming. He was old, weak, and deaf. I had to speak very loudly.

'My salaam to you, Waraqa ibn Nuwfal,' I shouted.

He struggled to his feet, stared at me from a distance and said, 'Zayd! You've changed. I would never have recognized you on the street.'

I hugged him, kissed his hand and his left shoulder respectfully, and handed him a basket of fresh figs covered by green leaves.

'Thank you, Zayd! How long has it been since I've seen you? A century? Your moustache is almost grey, but you look good. You walk proudly, like a Persian king's royal scribe.

'But what brings you here?'

'I've come to visit you of course, but I must confess I've been writing about Muhammad's life. And you are an integral part of it.'

Waraqa gave the basket of figs to the children, took his cane, and we strolled together through his large garden, past the vegetable patch planted in the shade of the trees.

After having talked about the current situation in Mecca, I said, 'Waraqa, could you tell me where you first met Muhammad?'

'Hmm, let me think, where was it? Oh, yes! I regularly saw

him on the market. You couldn't help but notice him, because his way of doing things was different than other youngsters. When you spoke to him, you were struck by his conscious choice of words. I was looking for help in my shop. My brother-in-law suggested I ask Muhammad. I talked to him, and the very next day he started working for me.

'Allow me this analogy: I was looking for iron, but I got gold. I needed an errand boy, and I got a future prophet. Once I got to know Muhammad better, I realized he needed me as a confidant, as an older brother. He worked in my shop for three years, but it was obvious to me that he did not find the work gratifying. He needed to travel to find himself. And I felt it was my duty to make that possible.

'I put him in contact with a friend of mine, a very successful merchant, and I recommended he send Muhammad on a trading mission. Muhammad was given the responsibility for seven camels loaded with goods. Not yet twenty years of age, he set out on the journey of a lifetime.

'He did this kind of work for four years, for several traders, and he became known as Muhammad the Truthful.'

'Why the Truthful?'

'He was extremely honest, and when it came to money he never cheated anyone. He led his trade caravans single-handedly, worked hard, and had a lot of drive. That's why all the merchants wanted to hire Muhammad.

'Zayd, I have an amusing story for you. Muhammad once had an appointment with a prominent trader, but the trader forgot and didn't show up. When the man arrived at his place of business the next morning, Muhammad was still there waiting for him. The trader offered him an important position in his company.'

'What kind of position?'

'That of caravan master. He would later be responsible for leading dozens of runners and hundreds of camels loaded with goods to distant cities.'

A new world opened up for Muhammad. The trips were long. He slept in caravanserais and met traders from the Persian Empire, Egypt, Ethiopia, and the Byzantine Empire.

That is how he became acquainted with Zarathustra of the Persians, Isa of the Christians, Musa of the Jews, and the Pharaohs of Egypt.

The mighty Persian Empire with its enormous wealth awakened something in Muhammad. In Mecca when we thought of the Persians, we thought of gold, gorgeous women, fruits, carpets, kings and queens, and their prophet Zarathustra.

Compared to the Persian Empire, our country was a backward place, a sandpit.

Every country once knew civilization. Not us, not ever.

Every civilization once had a Holy Book. Not us, not ever.

We still worshiped stone gods.

Mecca was a doomed city. Slaves were treated like cattle, and women were locked away in their homes, the property of men.

Muhammad travelled; he slept in Persian caravanserais and spent entire nights talking with other traders.

He clearly saw the differences and thought deeply about these matters.

12 Ibrahim, Muhammad's Example

Waraqa was not your average merchant. He was a free spirit who was aware of the corrupt social situation in Mecca.

He was a *Hanif.*

Hanif denoted a splinter sect of Christianity that did not follow the official teachings of the Church. The Hanafi felt that the Church had changed the contents of the Bible and the life story of Isa.

In the period Muhammad worked for Waraqa, this underground movement took root in Mecca. A group of young men, who knew the era of glorifying idols was over, met in secret. They opposed the slave traders and corrupt merchants. They wanted to improve the position of women and slaves in society. They were looking for a way to save Mecca from disaster.

Waraqa was an active member of this group.

Later on, once Muhammad no longer worked for him, Waraqa took him along to a meeting. Everybody welcomed Muhammad warmly.

'He was an asset,' Waraqa said, 'an expert debater and very charismatic. Yet, as time passed, I could see him slowly getting bored. He also didn't feel at home with us. Perhaps he thought we were too softhearted. We were interested in reform, while he was talking about revolution. He told us that we needed to openly take action against the idols. He didn't see the point of our secret meetings. He thought we should go out into the street to talk with people directly. This hadn't even occurred to us; we also didn't want to. We were looking for a simple solution for the city of Mecca, but Muhammad's thinking was way ahead of us.

'I didn't see it in him yet, because he was so young at the time, but I think even then he was looking to the divine for a solution. He never spoke openly about this. Maybe he wasn't ready. Though, in retrospect, I now see it very clearly. Muhammad wanted to save Mecca with a Book in his hand. The prophet Ibrahim was his example. Ibrahim belonged to the Arabs, unlike Musa and Isa.

'As a child, Muhammad had spent hours each day with his grandfather in the Kaaba, where traces of the prophet Ibrahim were ever-present.

'In addition, Ibrahim's tribe had once worshipped their idols in the building.

'Ibrahim was against the idols of his people; he wanted to do away with them. On one occasion, he even smashed the idols with an axe. Ibrahim was arrested and was going to be burnt at the stake.

'As he got older, Muhammad often thought of Ibrahim, and he became more and more obsessed with completing Ibrahim's unfinished task. He gradually started missing meetings, and later he pulled back completely. But in our group, he met three learned men who would accompany him until the end of his days: Abu Bakr, Umar, and Uthman.'

Abu Bakr later became Muhammad's direct successor, the first Caliph of Islam.

Umar followed Abu Bakr as the second Caliph, and Uthman became the third Caliph, after Umar.

Waraqa was an old man, and it was a warm day. He could no longer stand the heat and was ready for his afternoon nap. 'Shall I come back tonight, when it's a bit cooler?' I shouted in his deaf ear.

'That's fine. Come,' he nodded.

13 Khadija, Muhammad's First Wife

The merchant Waraqa did something else that dramatically influenced Muhammad's life. He introduced him to his wealthy, aging cousin, Khadija. By doing this, he pushed Muhammad out of the nest into the world so he could spread his wings and soar.

I was very curious about the story of Muhammad first meeting Khadija.

Khadija also changed my life. I was nothing, but I became something because of her.

When I write about her, I, Zayd, must choose my words carefully. She was the mistress of the house, the person who watched over me.

She was not my mother, but she could have been.

I promised myself that before committing a single word to paper about her, I would weigh my words carefully in my heart.

The honourable Khadija was the single most powerful businesswoman in Mecca.

She was my creator, the woman who purchased me as a slave and took me home. She made me who I am today.

To find out more about her, I returned to Waraqa's house that evening.

I was warmly received by his son. He had placed a bench against the wall in the courtyard for us. I sat down next to Waraqa.

'Waraqa, tell me about Khadija.'

'Yes, my charming cousin Khadija. You know, one never really forgets such things, but I'm so old, sometimes my memory needs a bit of help.'

'Waraqa, how did you get the idea to introduce Khadija to Muhammad?'

'My uncle, Khadija's father, was a prominent merchant in Mecca,' Waraqa said. 'He died unexpectedly. He didn't have a son, and therefore Khadija, his eldest daughter, took over the family business. It was in the period that Muhammad was working as a caravan master for the big traders.

'I thought Khadija could use someone reliable like Muhammad, as her right hand. So I talked to Khadija first, and afterwards, I approached Muhammad.

'At that time, there were only a few lavish homes in Mecca: houses that resembled a palace. One of these was owned by Khadija. I took Muhammad along and introduced him to her.'

'Did you expect them to marry?'

'No, Khadija was already in her early forties, had been married twice and given birth to four children. Muhammad was at least fifteen years younger than she was, and, as far as I know, had never touched a woman. What's more, Khadija was a Hanif, like me.

'No, I hadn't expected them to marry, and at first I wasn't happy about this. It somehow felt like betrayal. I wasn't the only one taken by surprise. When the other traders heard the news, they were amazed and gossiped among themselves. Nobody could fathom it, but eventually, I understood.

'I thought to myself, this Muhammad gets what he wants. In time, he will turn the world on its head. He grew up an orphan without any possessions and wanted to rid the Kaaba of its pagan gods single-handedly. Someone with such great ambition needed authority and power. Khadija gave him both. He needed an impressive house; Khadija's home was impressive. He needed a defining book; Khadija offered him her Hanifite Bible. He was a man who needed camels; she gave him three thousand camels and a few hundred labourers. Muhammad was illiterate; Khadija taught him to read.'

'Waraqa, it sounds like you're suggesting Muhammad married Khadija to chase his dream.'

'Is that how it sounds? Frankly, sometimes I think it was true—sometimes not. I still don't know what to think. A man of twenty-five can't possibly know he'll be a prophet one day. And Muhammad could have had any girl he wanted. Then, why choose Khadija? For the power, right? Or do you see it differently, Zayd?'

Instead of answering, I asked him another question, 'Waraqa, if I'm not mistaken, in the beginning you visited Khadija and Muhammad all the time but later you saw them less often. Why didn't you support Muhammad in his mission?'

'Look, Khadija gave her body, her mind, her gold, her house, her camels, and even her religion to Muhammad. I was a Hanif, I remained a Hanif, and I'll go to my grave a Hanif.'

'Your words sound bitter, Waraqa. Muhammad must have hurt you?'

'No, that's not it, he never did. If you wanted to follow Muhammad, you had to surrender to him completely—your mind as well as your wealth. You had to become one with him. I wasn't prepared to do that.'

There was a long silence, with no room left for words. I kissed Waraqa's hand and rose to take leave of him.

14 Samiha, Khadija's Daughter

Muhammad became the man of the house. He took control of the family's commercial interests, hired a few young, skilled, business-savvy individuals he knew from the past, and gave them enough freedom to do their work. The old family trade, which had received hardly any attention for a long time, was given a new impulse and became a vibrant business.

I needed to talk to someone who could tell me more about that period. Someone who had witnessed it up-close.

So naturally, I went to see Samiha, Khadija's daughter from her first marriage.

Samiha was twelve when her mother married Muhammad. She could still remember the first time young Muhammad visited their house.

'I'd never seen Muhammad before, so I hid behind a curtain to get a good look at him. He wasn't tall, but not short either. His long, milky-coloured shirt was brand new. He walked upright and wore closed leather shoes. He'd slicked back his black hair with oil, and it shimmered in the torchlight as one of the servants escorted him into the room to meet my mother. Because he was so young, my mother was shy and behaved awkwardly.

'It had always been very quiet in our house, but Muhammad breathed new life into it. My mother laughed again and our home was constantly filled with people.

'A few times a week, a group of men came for dinner, and afterwards they debated with Muhammad. There was plenty of eating, drinking, and talking.

‘In almost no time at all, my mother was pregnant and gave birth to a son. Muhammad was so happy; he beamed with joy. He was so proud of his son, he sometimes came home three times a day just to admire him. To everyone’s surprise, my mother got pregnant twice more and gave birth to two daughters. My mother—who had given up hope for a new family life after two failed marriages—now strut like a peacock through her house while the servants rushed from one room to another to take care of all the children.

‘Muhammad, who had never really known his own father and mother, was now the father of a large family.

‘Outside of the house he was busy with trading, and at home he gave his undivided attention to us—seven children—my mother, and the servants. He was young but also clever and wise. You felt safe in his presence.

‘But unexpectedly, disaster struck. Muhammad and Khadija’s son Qasim fell ill. Muhammad had each one of Mecca’s physicians come to our house to treat him—to no avail. The boy died in Muhammad’s arms.

‘Along with his death, happiness disappeared from our house—as if the lights were extinguished for good—that’s how dark our lives became.

‘Muhammad was immersed in grief. The man, who had interrupted his work three times a day to spend a few moments playing with his son, threw himself into the business and seldom came home to eat.

‘One day my mother went out by herself. She never went out alone; she always took some of her servants along. I remember it like yesterday; I shouted, “Mother, where are you going?”

“I’ll be back in no time,” she said.

‘She went to the house of her nephew, the slave trader

Hakim ibn Hizam. I don't know exactly what was discussed there, but when she returned, she had someone with her. A boy who looked about seven years old, barefoot, with long, dirty fingernails and tangled hair.

"Who's this, Mother?" I asked surprised.

'She didn't answer me, summoned her handmaiden and said, "Take him, cut his hair, wash him, cut his nails, put clean clothes on him, and keep him in your room until I call for you."

'Later that night, when Muhammad finally arrived home, my mother made him wait in the courtyard, "Stay here, close your eyes, and don't steal a peek."

'I can still see it—as if it was yesterday.

'Muhammad closed his eyes. My mother gestured to her servant and grabbed a torch.

"Muhammad, now you can look," my mother said, and she held up the torch. The boy with his bobbed hair, in his clean clothing, was shyly staring at Muhammad.

"And who's this?" said Muhammad, surprised.

"His name is Zayd. I bought him for you," my mother said smiling.

'A broad smile appeared on Muhammad's face. Happiness returned to our home. My mother got pregnant again twice and hoped to bear Muhammad a son, but she bore him two daughters. Zayd remained Muhammad's only son.'

I, Zayd, shed tears of joy as Samiha told me this story.

15 Khadija Reads Her Bible Aloud

Samiha's story took me back to that first night I spent in Muhammad and Khadija's house.

I can remember almost all the details. From the moment I was stolen as a child of five, at the marketplace in Ta'if, I spent two years living like a caged animal in the sheds of slave traders. After Khadija purchased me from her nephew, I was given my own bed in the servants' quarters.

I could not sleep that first night because my bed was so soft and clean. Everything was so different from what I was used to.

I had never seen a woman reading a book or a man laying his head in a woman's lap. There is also one particular occasion I have never forgotten.

It was a warm night, and the sky was dark blue and vast—the countless stars seemed to be hovering right above me. It looked like the stars were hanging from the roof, or as if the house was floating in their midst. Muhammad was lying on his back on a rug, with his head in Khadija's lap. She was reading to him from her Bible by the light of a lantern on a wooden table beside her. Muhammad listened quietly while their daughter slept on his chest. I did not know that their son had died recently and they were so sad because of this loss. Khadija was reading Muhammad a fitting passage to comfort him, to give him hope again, but I did not know that either.

The words she read him that night nestled in my heart. At the time, I did not understand what it was all about, but years later, I searched the Bible and found the passage. When I read it again, tears welled in my eyes:

> 'Then Pharaoh commanded all his people, "Every boy that is born to the Hebrews, you shall throw into the Nile, but you shall let every girl live."'
>
> 'Now a man from the house of Levi went and married a Levite woman. The woman conceived and bore a son; and when she saw that he was a fine baby, she hid him for three months.
>
> When she could hide him no longer, she got a papyrus basket for him, and plastered it with bitumen and pitch; she put the child in it and placed it among the reeds on the bank of the river.'

Reading the Bible aloud became a tradition at our house. Every night after dinner, a servant unrolled a carpet on the porch, fetched a table, set a lantern on it, and laid Khadija's Hanifite Bible beside the oil lamp.

She read aloud while Muhammad reclined on a large pillow and listened with his eyes closed. The servants quietly leaned out the windows listening. I always sat in the door opening.

In the Qur'an Muhammad proudly mentions, perhaps a hundred times, that he could neither read nor write. That is somewhat true, but also not.

It is true that when he met Khadija he could not read or write. After that, he tried to master reading, and he made concerted efforts to learn to write.

He wrote with his right hand, but his handwriting was hard to decipher. Like the scribbles of a child.

I can still remember Khadija teaching us to read and write.

She could not force Muhammad to practice. He simply did not do it. But I did; I had to, otherwise I was not allowed to go outside. I wrote so much that I got calluses on my fingers.

After a while, I was able to read as well as Khadija, but I cannot say the same for Muhammad. He read very slowly, stumbling on the words. He did not read whole sentences or words, but letters. And it is tiring to read letter by letter. Although he was known for his patience, he lacked the patience to read a text all the way to the end. He was not a reader; he was an orator.

16 Muhammad's Stay in the Caravanserais

The children had reached an age where Khadija could keep the household running smoothly by herself.

Muhammad employed a few experienced traders to run his business in his absence. This gave him the freedom to travel to faraway places. Sometimes he stayed away for months. He would send his caravan back with goods and stay on at a well-visited caravanserai near the border of the Persian Empire. This caravanserai was on the Silk Road.

It was Muhammad's favourite place. Later, when I was older and travelled with Muhammad, I once spent three weeks with him there.

It was an unforgettable experience. Merchants from all over the world stopped there with their caravans. They were the richest, most powerful, and most important merchants of their time. Not only the old, experienced businessmen of Yazd—the birthplace of the Persian prophet Zarathustra—travelled past the caravanserai, also Indian and Greek traders who had journeyed long distances on their camels.

Those merchants came not just to trade, they longed to travel—they wanted to see something of the wide world. These were the most significant journeys of their lives, and how they came to be acquainted with new developments in the world. They met people from other cultures and shared their stories and experiences.

Besides the merchants who came to the caravanserai, many scientists, poets, astronomers, and adventurers stayed there.

They rested for a while, got to know one another, and talked at length. Many spoke several languages; others arranged an interpreter on the spot.

During the day, the merchants focused on their businesses. They displayed their goods on the ground so others could see what they had brought with them.

It was a marvellous experience. In my entire life, I had never seen such a variety of wares. Weird and wonderful brass statues that the Greeks had brought, stunning writing paper that the Indians had carried all the way from China, new iron shovels and pickaxes offered for the first time by Byzantine craftsmen. And in addition: pearl necklaces, gold bracelets, carpets from Persian merchants, and all sorts of spices, dried fruits, and animal hides.

As night fell, and once everyone staying in the tents had eaten dinner, it was time for new magical scenes. People crowded together on the ground, forming dozens of circles. Torches burned; fresh tea was passed around. Those who sold delicacies handed out fresh sweets, and pipes were smoked.

In one circle, people played music, in another, beautiful slave girls danced. In a third circle, snakes and monkeys amused the crowd. A bit further down, at a quieter part of the caravanserai, scholars philosophized about their new insights concerning the world. Also, texts from the Bible, the Torah and the Avesta of Zarathustra were discussed. Poets read their recent work aloud, and astronomers drew the heavens—according to their newest findings—in different colours in the sand.

If it had been up to Muhammad, he would have never gone home.

With great interest, he listened to the scientists and astronomers and discussed the texts of the ancient prophets. He enjoyed the verses of the poets.

Once he returned home, he could count on a few days of quarrelling. Khadija shouted, 'Where were you, Muhammad? Don't you need us anymore? Or did you happen to forget you have a wife and children? Or do you think: that business isn't mine anyway; it belongs to my wife's family?'

Then, the silence returned to their daily lives. Muhammad went to work and came home on time, but I noticed something in him was different. He was quieter, and his eyes had more intensity. He grew thin, and deep creases appeared in his face.

'Muhammad, what's going on with you?' I often heard Khadija ask him.

He did not answer. It was like casting a stone into a deep hole.

17 The Five-Year Periods of Muhammad's Life

Khadija's daughter Samiha was already married at that time, but she came home regularly to visit. She had good contact with her mother.

'Sometimes I thought my mother married the wrong man yet again,' Samiha said. 'Everything was going well with the business, and we had lots of fun at home, but then he started taking those long trips. My mother was sad and thought Muhammad no longer wanted her. She was always afraid of losing him, that he would abandon her for a younger woman. She cried on my shoulder and said she was sure Muhammad was sleeping with other women.

'I believed my mother because she was now nearly fifty years old, and Muhammad was in the prime of his life. My mother talked to him, asked him about other women, but he always firmly denied this.

'My poor mother never had much luck with men. Muhammad was good to her, but she didn't have a moment's rest with him. The problems he caused, however, were not comparable to the sort of problems other men caused.

'Muhammad wasn't suited to be anybody's husband, and he certainly wasn't right for my mother.

'My mother later said that every five years a new phase in Muhammad's life began.

'The Muhammad who travelled far, stayed away for long periods, and drove my mother to despair, stopped travelling after five years. He became more restful, went to work on time, and arrived home on time. But he became withdrawn—extremely withdrawn. He was often deep in thought, and grey hairs appeared in his beard.

'He spent more time with his old friends and conversed with Abu Bakr, Umar, and Uthman well into the night.

'And there were the books. He came home with a large book, and every night Khadija would read to him from it. The books brought Muhammad back to my mother. She sometimes had Muhammad by her side the entire night, and I saw that she was happy again.

'After five years, he started going up into the mountains. Much to her dismay, he would sometimes spend the whole night there.

"Mother, let him be. You'll never have him all to yourself," I tried to console her.'

18 Muhammad and the Cave of Hira

There was a mountain range on the outskirts of Mecca, and when the sun shone, the slopes were vibrant yellow-brown in colour. In the winter, they looked black.

The large rocks were jagged and hard, without a single blade of grass. There were no trails. It was actually the realm of snakes, salamanders, and large caramel-coloured grasshoppers.

The other side of these mountains, where the shade fell in the afternoon, was covered in thorny plants. In the springtime, the shepherds brought their flocks there to eat from the fresh undergrowth.

The mountains were not very unique, but there was a cave that is now considered a divine place. That cave bears the name Hira.

Hira became an inseparable part of Muhammad's life and plays an important role in the Qur'an. It is the place where Muhammad first met the Angel Jabra'il, the emissary of Allah.

For five years, from age thirty-five to age forty, Muhammad regularly climbed Mount Hira.

And even if he was home more often than before, he wasn't actually present—he was emotionally absent.

He went about his work, but you could hardly say his presence was apparent. He withdrew to his room, closed the door, and locked himself away.

Khadija was worried about Muhammad and the family business. So she tried to involve herself more. She sent me to out to make appointments with other prosperous merchants. When Muhammad did not go to work, she went to his office instead, with me at her side.

'We can't count on Muhammad anymore,' Khadija told me. That was also the complaint of several other merchants. More and more Muhammad did not live up to his agreements; he did not deliver on time, and he did not pick up goods he had ordered.

Muhammad sought refuge in a cave on Mount Hira.

He did not tell us when he was leaving, and he did not tell us when he would return. It began with him departing in the afternoon, only to come back home in the deep of night. Later on, he sometimes stayed away for two or three nights.

Khadija once said to me, 'Zayd, we're losing Muhammad; you're the man of the house now. Pay close attention to everything, keep your eyes open, and listen carefully. Later, when you're grown-up, you'll have to run the family business.'

That would take some time. Besides, my sympathies lay more with Muhammad than with her. I would go through fire for Muhammad; I was his son; I was his shadow; I had become an extension of him.

When I was a boy, I was not aware of this. I realized later on how devoted I was to him, and it was because of Muhammad's personality.

'May I go see him in the mountains? Maybe he needs our help,' I said one evening. Muhammad had not been home for a few nights and Khadija was worried.

'Yes, that's fine, Zayd. But it's dark; you won't be able to see anything in the mountains.'

'The moon is shining. The night is clear, I'll be able to see everything,' I said.

I filled the saddlebags hanging on our mule with bread, fruit, dates, and water, and set out.

The mule could not go very far up the mountain, so I fastened its reins around a large stone and continued climbing to the top on foot.

The cave's location was tricky. I had to climb the mountain like a billy goat, paying close attention to my footing. The moon was gleaming in the middle of the night sky, a low-hanging expanse, blanketed with countless stars and with a silence so great, I did not dare move, afraid that a stone under my foot might make a sound. I finally reached the cave. It was an opening in a massive brown rock.

I softly called, 'Muhammad?'

I got no answer in return.

'Muhammad?' I cried once more.

Again no answer.

I cautiously crept into the cave. A small lantern was burning, but I did not see anybody. The cave was cramped. It was impossible to stand upright. You had to tilt your head a bit, but there was enough room for two men to sit down. A rug was lying on the ground, and several books, a pen, and some writings on parchment.

I immediately knelt to get a closer look at these, but it was as indecipherable as a secret code. I quickly flipped through the books. The Bible, the Torah, stories of ancient tribes, the teachings of a Persian prophet, and a few writings about the heavens. Were these actually Muhammad's books?

I placed the bag I had slung over my shoulder on the ground and went outside.

'Muhammad? Where are you, Muhammad?'

I climbed further, toward the mountain peak.

At the top, I saw the silhouette of a man gazing at the sky.

'Muhammad, is that you?'

19 Sayyid, Muhammad's Right-Hand Man

The only person who could tell me more about that period was Sayyid, an old business associate of Muhammad's.

They knew each other from the early days, when they were employed by the same merchant to lead his camel caravans.

When Muhammad married Khadija and took over her family's business, he convinced Sayyid to come work for him.

Sayyid gradually became Muhammad's right-hand man. Whenever Muhammad travelled to distant lands and stayed away for long periods, Sayyid was the person who took care of matters. Then when Muhammad started going up into the mountains more regularly, Khadija asked Sayyid to take charge of running the family business.

I had not seen Sayyid since my childhood. I did not know if he was still alive, but it was not hard to track him down. All the elderly merchants knew him and pointed me in the direction of Mecca's old bazaar.

Everything there had changed—of the traders I had known, nobody was left. Young traders, who knew nothing of those days, were now working where Muhammad's office had once been located.

Suddenly fate smiled on me. I spotted a man who used to bring tea around the bazaar with a jug on his back. His facial features were the same, but he had grown old and stooped.

'*As-salamu 'alay-kum*. Do you remember me?'

No, he did not recognize me.

'I'm Zayd, the son of Muhammad, who used to work here.'

The man smiled but apparently could not connect me with Zayd, that boy of fifteen.

I pressed a silver coin into his hand and said, 'I'm looking for Sayyid, who worked here for Muhammad. I want to know if he's still alive. I'll wait for you in that restaurant. If you find him, I have two more silver coins for you.'

It took a long time. I ate something, drank a few cups of tea, and ordered a water pipe. Just as I was dozing off, the man reappeared.

'And?'

'He's alive. He works in his grandson's shop.'

'What kind of a shop?'

'With sweets, on the other side of the bazaar, right by the corner archway.'

I followed the old tea vendor through the busy bazaar. The shop he spoke of was packed with customers. From a distance, you could already smell the delicious aromas of all sorts of Arabic sweets: cakes and candy, dried figs, dates, and raisins.

'Where can I find him?'

'He's at work in the back of the shop,' the tea vendor said. I handed him the two silver coins I had promised.

Indeed, Sayyid was sitting and kneading dough on a small wooden table. Although he was old, he looked good and worked at a quick pace. I placed my hand on his shoulder, leaned over, and softly said, *'as-salamu 'alay-kum*. I'm Zayd, Muhammad's son.'

His hands stopped moving, and he stared at me with his poor eyesight, 'Zayd? Zayd ibn Muhammad?'

He stood up and hugged me with his greasy hands, still flecked with bits of dough.

'It's too busy here, let's go outside,' he said, and we slowly walked to a tearoom garden where we could sit and talk quietly.

'Zayd! How did you find me?'

'With pieces of silver,' I said, laughing.

'What made you think of me?'

I told him what I was doing, that I was visiting people who had known Muhammad. 'Sayyid, tell me about those years when Muhammad regularly went up into the mountains and left business matters in your hands.'

'Your unexpected question throws me back in time. Drink your tea, Zayd. I need a moment to think … Well, to tell you the truth, I'm a bit disappointed in Muhammad.'

'Disappointed, why?'

'He ruled over a great realm,' Sayyid said. 'He was almost a king. Yet, he never sent anybody along to see how I was doing. Although we were still friends, and I'd worked for him all those years.'

'Sayyid, put yourself in Muhammad's shoes. He was so busy and everything happened so quickly; he didn't even have time for his own children.'

'I understand what you're saying. Muhammad and I were business associates, but also close friends who worked together,' Sayyid said. 'He was a noble man. More a leader than a businessman. Good at organizing things. A man capable of leaving his mark on the world, of achieving something great. Muhammad delighted in the changes taking place in Khadija's family business. He found the right men to work for him, sent large caravans all over the world, and gave structure to the company. However, he wasn't suited for selling spices or for exchanging silver for camel hides. He wanted to know more, to explore the world. In essence, he was busy with the future of Mecca. Through his encounters with other cultures, he understood that Mecca's very existence was threatened.

'After one of his distant journeys, he said to me, "The world is rapidly changing, but we're stuck in our old ways. In neighbouring countries, people speak admirably of their women, while we're ashamed of them and kill our newborn daughters. In civilized countries, children are treated with love, but we put them in cages like dogs and sell them at the market. Neighbouring countries have a prophet and a Book but we have neither."'

'Sayyid, can you tell me why he suddenly withdrew from everyday life and stayed in that cave?'

'Well, in those days, retreating into the mountains for a brief period to think quietly was considered normal. Scholars, astronomers, and philosophers did this too.'

'For a brief period,' I said. 'Muhammad did it for five years. Sometimes he spent weeks in that cave. I brought him food and water when he stayed away for long periods.'

'I know. Khadija was worried and came to see me; she thought Muhammad had gone crazy. Frankly, I thought so too. He didn't feel like working. Whenever he came to the office, he was preoccupied with the books he'd brought back from his travels.'

'I saw those books in the cave, but he couldn't read very well. What was he doing with all those books?'

Sayyid smiled. 'Muhammad could read just fine, but he was a slow reader. Up in the mountains he had all the time in the world. He probably read every single word of those books. Do you know when I first began to worry? When he told me he sometimes heard voices. That he'd heard someone calling, "Muhammad!" but he didn't see anyone. Whenever he was in the cave, that same voice returned, "Muhammad! *Qum fa-unzhur!* Muhammad! Get up! Go and dedicate your life to God; lead the people on the right path!"

'He went outside to look and saw no one.

'He said to me, "All our neighbouring countries believe in one God. I also believe that there is one Creator. When I look at the sea, I see Him. When I look at the mountains, I see Him. When I look at the fields, I see Him. Wherever I look, I see Him; the One and Only. But I don't understand why others don't see Him. Why don't people reflect? Why don't they ask themselves who made the heavens, the seas, the mountains, the bees, and women in all their glory? Who makes the rain fall from the sky? There must be someone. One God; the God who sent Musa, the God who sent Isa, the God who sent Ibrahim. There is one Creator. *There is only One and that is Allah, la 'ilaha 'illa llah.*"'

'So what you're telling me, Sayyid, is that Muhammad complained about hearing voices.'

'No, that's not what I said. He didn't complain. He really heard those voices. He thought someone from above was trying to reach him. He was waiting for that contact. That's why he went to the top of that mountain. To wait!'

20 Abu Na'im

After visiting Sayyid, I packed some bread, dates, and water, and headed for Mount Hira on foot. I wanted to experience a night in that cave the way Muhammad had.

As I got farther away from Mecca into the mountains, I had a better view of the city. I could still hear the sounds at first, but later they subsided. By now, I was the only one on the road beyond the city gate.

At the beginning of the evening, I started my climb.

Mount Hira looked miraculous at night. As I climbed, I was surrounded by an endless dark blue sky with twinkling stars and the moon's bright light.

Most of the mountain is easily accessible, but the last three large rocks before the top are difficult to maneuver. One needs to know exactly which way to go.

In the cave, I lit a candle. The spiders had spun webs, and there was a scattering of feathers on the ground. I brushed the ground clean and sat down.

I tried to read the book I had brought with me, but I could not concentrate. I was mesmerized by the mountain and the night.

For five long years, Muhammad had spent many nights here, and this is where he had heard the voices.

It was not surprising; everyone would start hearing things in this cave.

After some time, I blew out the candle and lay down on my side. I put my hands under my head as a pillow.

A few random thoughts about my childhood came to mind,

and I gradually became one with the night. I felt like I was floating with the stars in the firmament.

'Zayd!' a voice said, 'we have seen you.'

Tears welled in my eyes as I thought about how lonely Muhammad must have been all those years. He single-handedly wanted to save his people from destruction and looked to the heavens for help.

I inhaled deeply through my nose, as if I might actually catch a whiff of his scent.

But it was long gone. However, right above my head, in the cracks between the stones, there were still traces of smoke from his lantern that had burned on olive oil.

I could no longer stand being in the cave. I went outside and climbed further. When I reached the top, I saw something on the other side of the mountain that I had not expected, something that made me feel better. Dozens of herd animals were resting on the dark slopes, and there were wood fires with shepherds gathered around them.

It was so still, nobody moved, and it seemed like the herds, the shepherds, and their fires were all part of some grand universal scheme.

Imagine, Muhammad had witnessed this every night.

In his childhood, he had spent many years in the mountains herding sheep.

He must have had contact with the shepherds. He might have asked them for some milk. Perhaps he even ate a meal with them.

I walked from herd to herd to talk to the shepherds. They were all young. They knew nothing about the period Muhammad had spent in the cave. They suggested I talk to a few of the older shepherds. I returned to Mecca at the earliest light of day.

The next evening I went looking for shepherds who had been around in the old days, but they were all dead, or senile, or what they had to say was nonsense. Over the years, the harsh sun had taken a toll on their minds. Their memories were like shrivelled bunches of dates—except for one elderly shepherd who I found on his deathbed. His name was Abu Na'im, and he claimed he had often seen Muhammad in the mountains.

I knelt beside his bed, grasped his hand, and put my ear to his lips.

'I often ran into Muhammad in the mountains at night. He slept in that small cave. Sometimes I chatted with him in passing. Then I would ask him if he needed anything. All the shepherds knew him.'

'Do you have any idea how he spent his time in the cave?'

The shepherd closed his eyes and thought back for a moment.

'One night I saw him lying there. The cave was small. He was on his back with his feet against the wall and his arms clasped under his head.'

Abu Na'im was very weak and found it difficult to speak. I put a small piece of rock sugar in a glass of tea and helped him take a sip.

'What else can you tell me about Muhammad?'

'He often went walking late at night. He would join the shepherds and talk with them. Sometimes he sat like a wolf on top of the mountain. We saw his silhouette in the distance. It was a familiar sight for us. We didn't understand why he did it, but we'd seen more people do the same before him—wise men.'

'Was he always alone, or did people visit him?'

'I never saw him with anybody. As I said, occasionally he joined us, the shepherds, around the fire. We always spent a few months up on the mountain, and sometimes when he returned from the city, he brought us fresh fruit. In exchange we gave him milk, yogurt, or cheese we had made ourselves.'

I needed to let Abu Na'im rest. I gently squeezed two gold coins into the palm of his hand. I knew he would be happy with this because his time was near. Now he would have something to leave behind.

21 The Creator of Olives

I did not bother to look for any other old shepherds. I had a fairly good idea about how Muhammad had spent his time on the mountain.

As the chronicler, I was responsible for penning the story.

Nobody could help me better with this than Muhammad himself, and the best source was his Qur'an.

The Qur'an has one hundred and fourteen suras, each named after something that commanded Muhammad's attention.

Just to be certain, I jotted down some of the topics he spoke about in public: The Cow; The Ancient People of 'Ad and Thamud; The Early Prophets Musa, Nuh, and Ibrahim; The Women; The Table; The Cattle; Thunder; The Bees; Maryam; The Light; The Ants; The Spider; The Romans; Ornament and Splendour; Paradise; Hell; The Star; The Mountain; The Moon; Allah; Iron; The Pen; Humankind; The Angels of Death; The Night Star; The Sun; Honey; The Figs; The Seed; The Earthquake; The Ships; Olives; Early Morning.

There must be a Creator of all these marvellous things.

He who created humankind from a single closed drop of blood.

Who tamed the sun and the moon.

Who tamed the sea so that you might eat fresh fish and wear the ornaments you take from it.

Who caused humankind to sail in a fully laden ship, and created something in which they can sail.

Who attached the mountains firmly to the ground so that the earth would not cause you to sway.

He recited:

'By the running, fighting horses, their breath short and panting.
And by the sparks that fly from their hooves.
And by the warriors in the early morning.
Who then cause dust to rise.
And thus clear a path through the middle of the battle array.
There is truly something great, something mysterious going on.'

He stared at his pen, as if in a trance, and murmured:

'Nun wa-l-qalami wa-ma yasturun …
By the pen and what you write with it.
There must be a Creator of this miracle.'

Muhammad saw evidence of the Creator's greatness everywhere, but why didn't the Creator see him?

In his cave, he expected a sign from Him. Muhammad believed he was a chosen one, different from all the others. He felt he would receive a command from above. He could almost see He who ruled the world from heaven.

But nobody from above saw Muhammad or revealed anything to him.

Doubts arose in his mind. Muhammad began to think he was mistaken.

22 Jabra'il, the Emissary of Allah

If Allah, the Creator of humans, donkeys, bees, ants, apples, and dates was searching for Muhammad, he needed to make haste. Muhammad had just turned forty and was in the prime of his life.

But the doubt had taken its toll, had eaten away at him from inside. Muhammad looked thin and pale and had lost his appetite. He was not a prophet, nor a chosen one. Otherwise, the divine inhabitants of the heavens would have noticed him long ago. He had been so full of good intentions to change Mecca, but all in vain. The power he possessed to inspire others to follow the righteous path ebbed away.

The Creator had rejected Muhammad. He was probably not good enough for such an important task. He was lacking in the qualities possessed by the ancient prophets Ibrahim, Dawud, Musa, and Isa.

Who was Muhammad anyway? He was an orphan nobody wanted. He was an illiterate man who lived in his wife's house.

Muhammad was a nobody; a lost soul who had brought his wife's business to the brink of bankruptcy.

I can still remember the last fight Muhammad and Khadija had, which changed their lives forever.

'Muhammad, this is no life for you and also not for me. How long are you planning to stay in that cave? Until your beard is grey and reaches down to your knees?'

He did not reply; he just stared at the ground.

'Wait? How long are you going to wait? You have four daughters. If you go on like this, nobody will ask for their hands in marriage. Who is their father? A crazy fool in the mountains?'

He still did not reply, grabbed his coat, and hurried out the door to seek refuge in the mountains again.

I, Zayd, could not find anyone who knows exactly what happened that night on Mount Hira.

As a chronicler, I am not free to let my imagination run wild; I am compelled to stick to the facts.

The great poet Zeinolabedin Rahnema described that night in a masterful epic poem. Allow me to borrow his words:

'It was a Monday night in the month of Natiq, the seventeenth night. The moon shone softly bright, and it was peaceful. A gentle breeze was blowing. Some of the mountains were steeped in shadow; others were the colour of a camel's sandy coat. Mount Hira looked bigger and higher. It was as if the mountains were reaching for the stars, and the rocks had their ears pricked to detect any sound. A man was moving up on the mountain. It was Muhammad, climbing to the top in the moonlight. The higher he went, the more imposing the silence became. When he reached the top, he turned and gazed at Mecca, which was like a black hole in the distance. Mecca, where crimes were the order of the day, where the wails of newborn girls being slain could be heard, along with the laboured breathing of slaves working through the night. Now he could make out the large torches burning in front of the Kaaba. Oh, what a pity he was unable to change anything in the city.

'He gazed at the other side of the mountains, at the resting herds, the sleeping shepherds, the glowing embers of the fires. He did not see anything moving. He just kept staring. He could hear his heart pounding, his rapid breathing. Suddenly, a light appeared like a distant star. It got bigger and came closer. It grew wider, blocked out the sky, and descended. It encircled the mountains and engulfed Muhammad. He was startled, like a frightened dove. He trembled with excitement. He broke out in a cold sweat as the light took possession of him. He thought death was near, because something in his head began to spin and he heard a whispering sound deep in his ears, "Muhammad! Muhammad! Muhammad! Muhammad!"

"Who's that speaking?" Muhammad mumbled.

"The angel Jabra'il," said the voice.

"Jabra'il?" Muhammad replied with uncertainty.

"The angel Jabra'il," repeated the voice.

'A hand emerged from the midst of the light and held a piece of writing in front of Muhammad:

"'*Iqra'*, Muhammad! Recite these words, Muhammad!"

"I can't …" Muhammad said hesitantly.

"'*Iqra'*, Muhammad! *'Iqra'!*" the voice insisted.

"I can't …" Muhammad repeated

'The angel took him by the shoulders, shook him hard, and said, "'*Iqra'*, Muhammad!"

'With a wavering voice, Muhammad began to recite:

"'*Iqra' bi-smi Rabbi-ka lladhi …*
Recite in the name of Allah, the Creator.
He who created humankind from a single closed drop of blood.
Recite! Your God is the most loving.
He who taught humankind by the pen.
He who taught them what they did not know."

‘Once Muhammad had recited these words, the angel vanished as if he had never been there. Muhammad gazed helplessly at the sky.

‘Then he stumbled down the mountain.’

23 The Angel in the Room

It was very late at night, almost morning. I heard the front door in my sleep. I was the one who always waited for Muhammad, who always heard his footsteps first, who escorted him to his bedroom every night after he came home. I immediately knew something had happened. The door chain made an unfamiliar sound, and Muhammad's footsteps were somehow different than usual.

Something significant had taken place, and I would be the first one to know. Without delay, I grabbed a blanket and ran to the door.

In the darkness of the hallway, I saw Muhammad stagger. I wrapped the blanket around his shoulders.

A barefoot Khadija appeared beside me.

'What is it, Muhammad?' she said and led him to their bedroom.

I grabbed a torch and looked at Muhammad's face. Now I knew for sure.

'What has happened to you, Muhammad?' Khadija asked concerned.

'I … I … they … they … they came to me.'

Amazed, Khadija let go of Muhammad's arm. 'What did you say?'

'They … he … he had a piece of writing with him.'

'Who are you talking about?'

'He commanded me to read the words aloud, so I recited, *"'Iqra' bi-smi Rabbi-ka lladhi khalaqa.'"*

With tears in her eyes, Khadija helped her husband to their

room. 'Come, my beloved. Everything is going to be fine.'

I also had trouble restraining my tears.

But while Khadija wept about her husband's anguish, I cried with joy.

And with the torch in my hand, I lingered on the porch.

'Lie down here, my poor husband. Rest your head in my lap.' I overheard Khadija saying through the open window.

I waited until it was quiet. It would be impossible to sleep; it was almost morning anyway.

I went to the well and lowered the bucket. I needed a sip of fresh water.

Nobody can tell me more about what happened that night on the mountain.

Fortunately, witnesses are not necessary because Muhammad recounted the story in the Qur'an, in the sura 'The One Wrapped in a Mantle'.

Muhammad was still lying in Khadija's lap. He had pulled his coat over his head. Khadija assumed he had fallen asleep. But Muhammad was awake with his eyes shut, thinking back on his encounter with the angel Jabra'il.

Suddenly he heard the angel's voice again, '*Ya ayyuha l-muddathiru! Qum fa-unzhur …!* You, the one wrapped in a mantle. Get up! Lead the people to Allah, the One and Only!'

Startled, Muhammad pulled the coat from his head.

'What is it, Muhammad?' Khadija asked.

The angel is in the room with us,' he said, trembling.

'There's nobody here, just rest, my darling.'

'I haven't gone crazy; I hear voices, I hear him.'

'Muhammad, you need to rest.'

At dawn, Muhammad put on his coat and left the house. And I, Zayd, who was drawing water from the well at that early hour, followed him from a distance. On the Kaaba Square, he ran into his friends Abu Bakr, Umar, and Uthman.

'What is it, Muhammad? Didn't you sleep well?' Abu Bakr asked.

'La 'ilaha 'illa llah,' Muhammad said, 'I have been spoken to. Do I look like a fool? Do you think I see ghosts?'

Abu Bakr grabbed him by the arm, 'You're coming with us!'

So that she would not worry, I went and told Khadija, 'Abu Bakr, Umar, and Uthman have taken him to a safe place.'

24 Abu Bakr, Umar, and Uthman

Abu Bakr was older than Muhammad was. They had met doing business. He was a wealthy merchant who owned more than a thousand camels. He later succeeded Muhammad as the first Caliph.

Umar was younger than Muhammad was. He traded in jewellery and gems, primarily diamonds and pearls. He later succeeded Abu Bakr and conquered the Persian and Byzantine Empires.

Uthman was also younger than Muhammad was. He came from a wealthy family that was involved in politics. Uthman had a shop in Mecca that sold Yemini silk, Byzantine satin, and colourful Persian curtains decorated with motifs of suns and lions. He later succeeded Umar.

Certainly everyone was free to think Muhammad was crazy or going crazy, but these three friends of his thought otherwise.

They often got together to discuss religion, Mecca, and the idols. But Muhammad gradually withdrew from them. After every long trip abroad, his arguments were more persuasive, and he spoke with more conviction about the rightness of his path.

Abu Bakr, Umar, and Uthman had serious doubts about whether Muhammad, with his Allah, could bring about change in Mecca. He was not the first who had tried.

The people of Mecca were used to seeing an occasional

crazed person, a poet, a half-baked philosopher, publically proclaiming, 'I am a prophet who has come to show you the way.' But they now realized that Muhammad was unstoppable, like a large stone tumbling down a mountain slope. He would destroy either himself or the idols.

I was curious about what Abu Bakr, Umar, and Uthman had said to Muhammad that morning.

One of them should actually answer this question, but that is unlikely. They were the ones who made Muhammad untouchable. They attributed qualities to him that he did not have.

So, unfortunately, the part of Muhammad's life that is only known to Abu Bakr, Umar, and Uthman, will remain unknown to me.

25 Ali, Muhammad's Cousin

Ali was the youngest son of Uncle Talib, the man who had adopted Muhammad. Essentially, Ali was Muhammad's younger brother.

He later became the fourth Caliph, the successor of Muhammad.

We were trusted friends, and I could speak to him in confidence.

In the mosque, where Ali was leading the prayers, I found a place right behind him. When the praying was over, I kissed him on the shoulder.

'What brings you to us, Zayd?' he asked, smiling.

Ali knew I was committing the story of Muhammad's life to paper, and he had already said I was always welcome if there was something I wanted to know. So I said, 'I have a question that only one person can answer.'

'What's your question, Zayd?'

'Ali, you know Abu Bakr, Umar, and Uthman like the back of your own hands. What could they have said to Muhammad when they ran into him on the street in a state of bewilderment?'

The faithful had left the mosque; the two of us were alone. The custodian brought us tea and dates.

'I've often heard them describe that morning,' Ali said, 'it has become a treasured memory. The story goes like this. At first, they thought Muhammad had quarrelled with Khadija and left her house for good. Then Muhammad surprised them with his words:

"'*Iqra' bi-smi Rabbi-ka lladhi* …
Recite in the name of Allah, the Creator.
He who created humankind from a single closed drop of blood."

'The minute they heard him utter this, they grabbed him by the arm and whisked him off to Abu Bakr's house. They made him a hearty breakfast of milk, fried eggs, cheese, and honey. Once he felt slightly revived, Abu Bakr said to him, "Tell us everything, Muhammad."

"They reached out to me," Muhammad replied, and he drifted away deep in thought. Then encouraged by Abu Bakr, Muhammad told them the rest of the story.

'After a long silence, Umar said, "Your destiny awaits you, Muhammad."

'Then Abu Bakr said, "You're not crazy, Muhammad, but if you stop now, you'll go crazy. Your only choice is to go on, until the bitter end. I'm here for you."

"I am too," Umar concurred, "but there's one problem. Now you're a prophet, but what are we? You have actually made us irrelevant; we are not useful to you like this."

"In any case, not yet," Uthman added, "but we'll stay in the background. We'll just see how it goes. I wish you well, Muhammad."

'Abu Bakr closed by saying, "Blessed be your journey. We support you, in sorrow and in joy!"

'Umar kissed Muhammad on his right shoulder.

'Uthman kissed Muhammad on his left shoulder.

'Abu Bakr kissed Muhammad on his forehead.

'And they all rose.'

26 Muhammad, the Messenger

Muhammad spent an entire year trying to convince people that he was the messenger of Allah.

And I followed him everywhere he went.

First, he visited people he knew.

I kept my distance. I could not hear what he was saying to them, but I saw him pointing to the heavens and in the direction of the Kaaba.

I could tell when he was talking about the ancient prophets. From certain hand movements, I knew he was talking about neighbouring countries where people did not worship idols.

I knew he would tell them about Mount Hira next, about the angel he had met.

These people respectfully received Muhammad because they knew him, but nobody really listened.

He spent a year going from one place of work to another talking to his former colleagues, but at the end of that year still nobody believed him.

'Allah? What Allah? What are you talking about, Muhammad?' They laughed at him. They had seen these kinds of self-appointed prophets come and go.

'Muhammad, we might have expected this from someone else,' they said, 'but never from you. You're a decent man, Khadija's husband. You run a big company. How is it possible that you're suddenly going door to door like a lunatic to warn people? You, a messenger? Where did you get such an idea?'

Namim bin Nasir, a dealer in salt, pepper, and spices, told me the following, 'When Muhammad appeared in the bazaar, traders would go hide in the storerooms behind their shops, because if he caught a glimpse of them, he'd start ranting about Allah and about the rain, the apple, the dates, the seeds … he just wouldn't stop.'

This Namim still remembered a conversation he had with Abu Jahl, Mecca's chief of public order, 'Abu Jahl came into my shop and said, "I just bumped into Muhammad on the street. Or to be more accurate, he waylaid me and proceeded to give me an earful. He said, 'Abu Jahl, if you follow me, you'll be the warlord of Allah's army.'

"I made a joke and said, 'And if I perish?'

"Muhammad answered, 'If you fall in battle, you'll go to paradise where virgins in green dresses, wearing gold bracelets, and holding cups of wine await you on couches in the cool shade of the trees.'"

'Abu Jahl laughed loudly and continued, "Muhammad's beard has turned grey, and his business is bankrupt. So now he's trying to sell us virgins."'

27 The Second Year of Muhammad's Mission

More and more often, Muhammad could be found at a corner of the Kaaba Square waiting for passers-by. Perhaps somebody he knew, or somebody who might be willing to have a conversation with him.

He would approach that individual and stroll alongside him. I would follow right behind.

I was glad when the conversation lasted for a while, but these kinds of discussions were mostly futile.

If people were not interested, he would shake their hand, thank them for their time, and let them be on their way.

'Stone,' Muhammad would say to me, 'they're made of stone, just like their idols. They hear nothing. Their eyes, their ears, their mouths are petrified. When I talk to them, they refuse to budge even an inch.'

Some people insisted on proof.

'Muhammad, we know you as a sincere man, so prove to us that you're really a prophet. Show us some kind of confirmation from your Allah, even if it's only a note with a seal. After all, it should be simple for a Creator who fashioned the entire universe to give you a note.

'All the ancient prophets performed a miracle. Musa threw his cane on the floor, and it moved like a snake. Isa raised the dead to life. And you, Muhammad? What do you have as proof? Where's your miracle?'

Muhammad did not have a miracle, and as long as he could

not work miracles, he could not sell his Allah to these merchants.

There was also a grain of truth in what they were saying. He did everything for Allah, but Allah did nothing for him.

In the evening, Muhammad returned home exhausted.

Perhaps nobody else noticed it, but I saw his hair getting greyer by the day and the lines in his face growing deeper.

He no longer talked to Khadija about his mission. What was there to say, besides, 'Today nobody was interested in my message either.'

I admired Khadija for her patience. She quarrelled with him, but her anger was short-lived. She did not make him feel guilty. She took good care of him. Every night she tended to Muhammad's blisters.

'You need the blacksmith to fit the soles of your feet with horseshoes,' she lovingly teased him.

Working in the background, Abu Bakr, Umar, and Uthman did everything they could to find Muhammad followers.

First, they arranged private audiences between Muhammad and their friends, but none of those meetings amounted to anything.

Later they organized gatherings in Abu Bakr's house.

They would then give a feast with food, wine, fruit, and other delicacies. Afterwards, Muhammad would speak. The guests asked questions that led to heated discussions, like those you have at night in the Arabian Desert. They headed home drunk in the early morning hours, and the next day, they did not want anything more to do with Muhammad or his message.

Yet, Abu Bakr and Umar managed to win over two men for Muhammad. One was Abu Bakr's butcher, Zubayr. The other man was Sa'd, a small-time dealer in pearls and a business associate of Umar's.

A butcher and a pearl trader were the result of two long years of hard work. The situation could not continue like this.

28 At His Wits End

Something strange was going on. Why had Allah only contacted Muhammad once?

Allah had given Muhammad the task of leading the people to Him, but He had not lifted a finger to help.

Did He not see how much pressure Muhammad was under?

Did He not see how people ridiculed him, and how Muhammad had risked everything for Him?

Did Allah not see how Muhammad had caused his children, his family, his wife, his friends, and his clan embarrassment by making a fool of himself, by proclaiming wherever he went that Allah was the Creator of the light and the Maker of the mosquito?

Was Muhammad really on the right path?

Muhammad's doubts returned.

Had Allah really approached him?

Had the angel Jabra'il actually held that piece of paper in front of Muhammad's eyes?

Perhaps it was a daydream; a fantasy?

And even worse, if this was not some figment of his imagination, then why had Allah not given him any proof, and why was he unable to perform miracles?

How could you appoint someone as your messenger without giving him a shred of evidence?

Days, weeks, and months elapsed without a sign from above.

Muhammad's doubting took its toll on him.

He left the city and went up into the mountains. He waited in front of the cave for a new sign, but no sign came.

So it was true, he had been mistaken; he had imagined everything. The Creator had never reached out to him. Allah did not need Muhammad.

That night, deeply disappointed, he went and lay down in the cave. He rested his head on a flat stone, curled up in a fetal positon, and began to cry.

Suddenly, he heard footsteps, followed by a voice, 'Muhammad!'

It was the angel Jabra'il:

'In the name of Allah
By the radiant day.
And by the night in which one rests.
Your Creator has not abandoned you and has not forgotten you.
He shall uplift you so that you feel happy.
Did He not find you an orphan and give you shelter?
Did He not find you lost and give you guidance?
Did He not find you needy and give you prosperity?
Come, Muhammad. Get up!'

Nobody would stop Muhammad now. He left the cave, descended the mountain, and threw himself into his mission.

'I don't need proof,' he cried out in the darkness.

'I am the proof.'

29 Muhammad Regains His Strength

Muhammad was full of strength when he returned home.

I grabbed the torch to get a better look at his face. It was obvious that he had spoken to the heavens again.

'Go and draw a bath for Muhammad,' I ordered one of the servants.

Muhammad entered Khadija's room in such a frenzy that he startled her.

'What has happened, Muhammad?'

'He … up there … the Angel … I … I received a new text,' he said. Muhammad's hands were trembling.

'What kind of text?'

'By the night in which one rests.
By the radiant day.
Your Creator has not abandoned you.'

Khadija rose and gently took his arm, 'Just calm down, Muhammad. Tell me exactly what happened.'

The next day, Muhammad's everlasting journey began. And he took all of us along with him: his daughters, his wife, our house, me, his uncle, his clan, all the women, all the Jews, all the slaves, all the camels, and all the idols.

His friendly approach had not worked. He decided to stand on a stool on the street and speak to the people to warn them. He had no other choice.

Ibrahim ibn Zajda Zahari told me about one of Muhammad's first speeches in public.

'Well, I didn't experience the moment with my own eyes,' Ibrahim ibn Zajda Zahari said, 'but I heard it with my own ears from Jahya abi Ashat, and Jahya abi Ashat heard it with his own ears from Ismail ibn Eyyas, and Ismail ibn Eyyas heard it with his own ears from his father Eyyas ibn Qasim, who experienced it first-hand. So when I tell you about this, I'm actually quoting Eyyas ibn Qasim:

"I traded spices in those days. With all my wares loaded onto one camel, I walked from village to village. On the way to Mecca, I visited Talib. He was a small-time trader like me, but he had three camels. Talib was Muhammad's uncle.

"I swear by Allah that I was standing there talking to Talib when a man of around forty suddenly emerged from a tent. He gazed at the sun setting over the desert. With water from a bucket, he washed his face, then his hands up to his elbows, and then his feet up to his ankles. He turned to the sun, his hands resting on his belly. Then man mumbled something, bent forward, knelt, and put his head on the ground while he hummed something else.

"I looked at Talib in surprise and asked, 'Who's that?'

'My nephew, Muhammad.'

'What's he doing?'

'He thinks he's a messenger. He wants to conquer the Persian Empire and bring the gold treasures of their kings here.'"'

Ibrahim ibn Zajda Zahari's story was about one of Muhammad's first prayers. It was not a finished prayer yet. Muhammad was still working on it; he was not sure how it should end.

On a number of occasions, I found Muhammad in a strange

position in his room at home. He was squatted on his hands and knees with his forehead on the ground.

Later on, he did the same thing on the veranda.

Khadija gave me a puzzled look.

'He's praying,' I said.

At that time, a number of texts were revealed to him in rapid succession. They were powerful stories, with a touch of the poetic. Sometimes they had the flavour of young dates, other times the taste of wheat:

'By figs and olives.
By Mount Sinai.
And by Mecca, the city of peace.
We have created humankind in the fairest form.'

One night when we were at Abu Bakr's house together with Umar and Uthman, Muhammad said:

'A new sura has been revealed to me.'

Every time he said this, they would sit upright, anxious to hear what he was about to say.

'Tell us, then,' Abu Bakr said.

Muhammad recited:

'In the name of Allah
All praise to Him, the Creator of the worlds.
The King of life after death.
We pray to you, and we ask only Your help.
Lead us on the right path.
On the path of those You have granted grace, not on the path of those You do not favour or who have gone astray.'

When he was finished, no one responded. With their heads bowed, they considered his words.

'This is no ordinary sura,' Muhammad said, 'but a prayer. I've been commanded to practice it in public.'

'What do you mean by practice?' Abu Bakr asked.

'People pray to their idols in the Kaaba. I'll pray to Allah. Tomorrow is Friday. In the early evening, it will be busy on the Kaaba Square. I'm going to pray there.'

'Where exactly on the square?' Abu Bakr asked.

'There on the ground.'

'What do you mean?' Umar asked.

'Everybody faces the Kaaba. Not me. I'm going to face the sun.' Muhammad said.

I was on edge the entire next day.

Muhammad said nothing. He had put Abu Bakr, Umar, and Uthman in a difficult position.

Would they join him in prayer?

If they did, they would be putting their lives on the line and be bound to Muhammad forever. If they did not, the question would arise as to whether Muhammad really had their support.

Toward evening, when the sun went down, Muhammad and I stood together on the Kaaba Square. My heart was pounding in my throat. Would they show up?

The courtyard was busy with people, and everybody was entering the Kaaba to pray. I was keeping an eye on everything. I hoped they would not forsake Muhammad at such a decisive moment.

The guards lit the square's large torches.

In the torchlight, I saw Abu Bakr approaching us. I trembled with joy. Oh, great God of Muhammad! And then Umar, Uthman, Zubayr the butcher, and Sa'd the pearl trader also appeared.

'Muhammad, they're here,' I whispered. 'All five of them.'

One by one, they embraced Muhammad. And I felt like something great was going to happen that nobody could stop.

'Let's begin,' Muhammad said.

He turned his back on the Kaaba and faced the setting sun.

Abu Bakr took the spot behind him.

Umar stood to the right of Abu Bakr.

Uthman stood to the left of Abu Bakr.

In turn, Zubayr and Sa'd took the places behind them.

I went and stood behind all of them.

'In the name of Allah,' Muhammad said loudly, and he recited the sura. We calmly repeated his words. Everybody was staring at us.

'What are they doing?'

'That's Muhammad in front,' somebody said.

'I see Abu Bakr,' another said.

'And the butcher.'

'And the pearl trader.'

'Why are they bending over like that?'

'Why are they pressing their foreheads to the ground?'

'What are they humming?'

Until well into the night, everybody was talking about Muhammad.

That night, Mecca did not sleep.

30 The People Mock Muhammad

Each day I took the stool and went out on the street with Muhammad.

I positioned it on the square when people were heading toward the Kaaba to pray.

First I climbed on top and announced, 'People! Muhammad, Allah's messenger, is here to speak to you.'

Then Muhammad stood on the stool and cried, 'You, my fellow Meccans. Don't ask your idols for help. They can't hear you. They are graven images of wood and stone.'

The people got angry. 'You, Muhammad. Your grandfather, the father of your grandfather, and the father of the father of your grandfather were keyholders of the Kaaba. You cannot insult our gods without insulting your deceased ancestors.'

'Idols can't be offended. They're deaf. They're blind and dumb,' Muhammad answered.

I moved the stool to a busy spot on the market square and shouted, 'People, Allah's messenger is here to warn you.'

Before Muhammad could even begin, they spoke to him in a harsh tone, 'Muhammad, you cause great unrest among the people of Mecca with your Allah. If you speak the truth, show us a sign from this Allah.'

'Take the olive,' Muhammad said, 'you can eat it, as well as press it and use its oil to light your lanterns. The olive's clear oil is a sign.

'Or take the camel on which you ride. That is also a sign.'

People started shouting at one another, 'What is he talking about? Olives and camels? He plays with words; he speaks nonsense. If he's telling the truth, why doesn't his Allah send an angel from heaven to help him? He isn't a messenger; he's human, just like us—he eats, he sleeps, and he washes himself in the river, like we do.'

I moved the stool to the square where camels were traded and cried out, 'Listen people, a new sura has been revealed to the messenger.'

And Muhammad started to recite:

'Did We not create the earth as a cradle?
And the mountains as giant pegs?
We created you in pairs.
We designated sleep for your rest.
We made the night as a garment for you.
We made the day so that you might go in search of bread.'

'What are we supposed to do with that cradle and those giant pegs?' asked a camel dealer.

'It was revealed to him,' another said.

'What a bunch of rubbish. Fantasies!'

Every Friday morning, I placed the stool alongside the road people travelled to bring their sacrifices to the great idol al-'Uzza.

Muhammad called, 'Men. You shouldn't be ashamed of your daughters.

'You mustn't sacrifice your newborn daughters to al-'Uzza.

'Allah has forbidden this.'

After the men had offered their sacrifices, they quarrelled

with Muhammad, 'You've gone too far. It's better if we never see your face here again.'

I placed the stool at the horse market and cried out, 'Allah's messenger is here.'

The people gathered around Muhammad. 'Muhammad, I don't understand why this Allah has chosen you as his messenger. You, who can barely read and write,' said one of the horse traders.

'I don't know either,' Muhammad said, 'Allah knows. He is all-knowing.'

'Muhammad, you say that Allah knows everything and can do everything. Ask him then to drop a few gold coins at my feet,' another horse trader said.

'People, I cannot perform miracles,' Muhammad said, 'I'm merely a messenger.'

'He doesn't know anything; he can't do anything,' the people concluded, and they went on their way, leaving Muhammad standing there all alone.

When the people saw that Muhammad continued with his warnings, even though nobody took him seriously, they began to mock him. They ridiculed him. They stuck their fingers in their ears and jokingly pulled their coats over their heads. And when Muhammad proclaimed Allah's name, they shouted the names of their idols: Wadd, Suwa', Yaghuth, al-Lat, Nasr, Asaf, al-'Uzza.

Then they pushed and shoved one another until someone bumped against Muhammad, and he fell from the stool. But Muhammad patiently took his place on the stool again and cried out, 'I'm not asking anything of you. I don't say these things for myself. I've been instructed to lead you on the right path.'

'But Muhammad, where does that path lead?' a man laughingly retorted.

'He's going to take us to paradise, to lie with the wanton maidens,' another man bellowed.

One evening when Muhammad was standing on his stool again, somebody hurled a stone at him. It hit Muhammad in the head and landed at my feet.

31 Al-A'sha, the Great Poet of Mecca

While most people mocked Muhammad, there were also those who silently listened to what he had to say. Al-A'sha, the great poet of Mecca, was one of them.

When I was a child, I once saw him riding through the streets of Mecca on a brown Arabian stallion. He looked like a king. He was wearing a cloak made of gazelle hide, embellished with jewels. He wrote magical poems about nighttime in the desert, about snakes, and women. And he composed verses about wine and about camels drifting like boats across waves of sand.

Whoever saw him perform never forgot him. His poetry was written in large letters on parchment with ox blood, and hung on the wall of the Kaaba.

When Muhammad was young, he was one of his great admirers. Whenever al-A'sha recited his poems, Muhammad always found a spot up front, and he knew many of the poems by heart.

I initially thought al-A'sha was dead, but I found him living in an old castle outside the city. His horse had died long ago. And his royal robes probably no longer fit him, given he was shorter, stooped over, and walked leaning on a gold-headed cane.

Perhaps nobody remembered his poems nowadays. But I did. And I greeted him in his sunny garden.

'*As-salamu 'alay-kum*, al-A'sha, the poet,' I called out and bowed my head.

With his frail hand, he shielded his eyes from the sun to get a better look at me.

I began reciting one of his poems from memory:

'Grapes turn black
After they ripen green
And they turn sweet, having been sour.
But the women of the desert
Stay brown forever,
A sweet shade of brown!'

He was beaming with joy.

'Who are you? You who have made me so happy?' he asked.

'Your admirer, Zayd. The *katib*, the messenger's scribe.'

'Which messenger?'

'Muhammad, the messenger.'

'Oh Muhammad,' he said, shaking his head in dismay.

He gestured to his servants with his cane. A male slave came and placed two chairs in the shade of the tall trees, and a female slave brought us a bowl of sugared water with rose petals.

'Have a seat,' he said, pointing to one of the chairs with his cane.

I sat down, but he continued to stand.

'So tell me …' he said.

'I'm putting Muhammad's life story on paper. It would be an honour to include the wisdom of the master al-A'sha in my book.'

The great poet al-A'sha took his time before speaking, 'At first sight, that Muhammad of yours was like the many false prophets of Mecca. People saw him as a respectable figure who suddenly went crazy. But he was different from the others. He knew what he wanted and had not only a boundless imagination; he was extremely determined. He had a plan, but his plan was flawed. He wanted a transformation from above. He tried to get the wealthy traders to unite behind him to destroy the idols in the Kaaba. But he was mistaken. His plan backfired. If you want to get rid of the idols, one should not ask the traders for help, and certainly not beg the powerful slave owners for their assistance.

'Muhammad was smart; he realized his plan was flawed. He altered his approach and turned to the slaves and the women. This radical change was a brilliant move. In our long history nobody had ever counted on the support of women. Suddenly, like magic, he pulled a mighty militia out of his sleeve. He gathered an army of slaves, the poor, and the women, and called it Allah's army.

'It was an extremely clever move on his part.

'Everybody continued to mock him, "Hey prophet! Where's your miracle?"

'For a long time, he couldn't say anything more than a modest, "Forgive me. Allah has not seen fit to give me a miracle."

'And that was his weak point, actually his weakest point. So I gave Muhammad a helping hand. But nobody knows this. I often went secretly to listen to him when he warned the people. I saw that his back was up against the wall because he couldn't produce a miracle. One night I sent my servant to him. I'd told him to whisper the these words in Muhammad's ear. "Muhammad, your suras are your miracle."'

I, Zayd, got tears in my eyes when al-A'sha told me this.

'Muhammad understood what I was saying,' al-A'sha continued, 'because the next day his response to the crowd was surprisingly bold.

"Muhammad, where is your miracle?"

"Listen to the tales I tell. The Qur'an is my miracle!" he cried out with conviction.

'Muhammad was truly a clever messenger. But what was he talking about? He didn't have a Holy Book. There wasn't even talk of a Book yet. He spit out some words, and they worked wonderfully. He said whatever came to mind; he wasn't concerned with being consistent. Nonetheless, those figments of his imagination were refreshing and poetic.

'Muhammad even went further and declared, "Nobody is capable of creating a Book better than the Qur'an, because the words I speak aren't my words but those of Allah. And everything I say can be found in the book *In the Beginning*."

'I couldn't stop myself from laughing aloud. Which book *In the Beginning*?

'He insisted that all his utterances were originally Allah's thoughts. In this way, Muhammad gave a divine quality to his own words.

'But it was only me, al-A'sha, the old poet of Mecca, who knew that Muhammad was indeed busy with a wondrous book. His language was new, his prose shockingly refreshing, yet he also committed plagiarism—stole the ancient stories of other nations and gave them a beautiful Arabian flavour. In this way, he made the texts his own.

'Muhammad's verses are not meant for those who want to quickly glance through a text, and without an understanding of the Arabic language, they seem rather chaotic.

'His stories are good for two types of people: illiterates and scholars. You have to keep repeating his words until they go to your head, like a fine wine.

'I don't know what people will think of Muhammad's tales a hundred years from now, but in this day and age, I envy him for his exquisite prose. The Qur'an is the miracle of our time.

'Whenever I have one of his suras in my hand, it feels like I'm embracing a wild swan that I must hold firmly against my chest.'

32 Allah, Islam, Qur'an

Al-A'sha was momentarily lost in thought. Perhaps he was trying to imagine what it would actually be like to embrace a wild swan. Then his attention returned to me.

'I envied Muhammad, secretly,' al-A'sha said, 'I didn't defend him, but I also didn't renounce him. I remained silent; I listened. A large part of what Muhammad said seemed like nonsense to me, but he expressed this nonsense in a new Arabic language. I still find it difficult to understand how he achieved so much with his incomprehensible words.

'Out of the nothingness, Muhammad called out, "*Allahu 'akbar*, Allah is Great!"

'Who is this Allah? And how do you know he is great?

'Allah was a new concept, and His greatness had yet to be established.

'Muhammad said, "*La 'ilaha 'illa llah:* there is only One: Allah." The form and composition of his statements were new. *Lah* in Allah means no or no more. Thus Allah is One and no more.

'He said, "*as-salamu 'alay-kum!* My salaam for you."

'Nobody had ever used salaam as a greeting, "*as-salamu 'alay-kum!*"

'The first time you say "*as-salamu 'alay-kum*" to someone, it tastes so very sweet, like biting into a fresh pastry.

'He said, "*Lam yalud wa-lam yalid*: He was not fathered, nor does he father."

'I felt my heart race the first time I heard these words. However simple—it was a commanding Arabic sentence with many *l*'s and *a*'s. When you say it, somehow it feels like you're talking about majestic mountains.

'The word "Islam" was also new. It didn't mean anything at first but as time passed, it came to mean: "Surrender!"

"Fine," said the people. "But to whom must we surrender?"

"To the Maker of all things!" Muhammad said.

'The word "Qur'an" also had no meaning. Later, it came to be understood as: "piece by piece; one after another; a piece of text now; a piece of text later. Read it and recite!"

'Muhammad was extremely determined, almost possessed. What he claimed was strange, and what he did was even stranger.

'He lied; he lied a lot. And he wholeheartedly believed his own lies. Perhaps lying is too harsh a word. Let's just say he invented things. He claimed that his Qur'an texts were revealed to him. But he made it all up—on his own, in his mind, and I enjoyed his powerful imagination.

'Still, there was always something disquieting in Muhammad's message. He was a remarkable man, without a doubt, and what he claimed sounded good, but why did he attach himself to the heavens with an imperceptible thread, to an imaginary Allah?

'He wanted to set a revolution in motion. And he'd delivered an unprecedented achievement in the Arabic language. He was a talented leader, so why did he behave like a dispossessed, fake prophet?

'Did he really believe he was a messenger? That all those texts were revealed to him?

'It's a difficult question to answer. It remains a mystery and that's why he's such an enigmatic figure. Still, he was so fixated on his Allah that he became one with his Allah. He was Allah.

Thus he created divine texts. Still, there are many, in fact a great many, beautiful texts—the most beautiful passages are when he makes a vow:

> "By the sun and when it shines.
> And by the moon when it follows.
> And by the day when it is illuminated.
> And by the night when it covers all things."

'Later he swore by figs and olives:

> "By the night when it veils all things.
> And by the day when its shines brightly.
> And by He who created male and female.
> And by figs and olives."

'And still later he swore by the horses:

> "By the running, fighting horses, their breath short and panting.
> And by the sparks that fly from their hooves.
> And by the warriors in the early morning.
> Who then cause dust to rise.
> And thus clear a path through the middle of the battle array."

'And he swore by the numbers, even and uneven.'

'What more do you need to know, Zayd?' al-A'sha asked.

I did not ask anything else. Instead, I recited one of al-A'sha's own poems for him:

'When you move
The world follows
Your lead.
While I gaze breathlessly
At your bare feet
In the brown sand
You, the world.'

I had made al-A'sha 's day.

It was also a day that would stay with me forever.

33 The Men of the Family

The residents of Mecca went out of their way to avoid Muhammad. And the merchants ordered their servants to bar him at the door. But people underestimated Muhammad. They still did not understand that he would not be deterred. He would keep going until the bitter end.

Muhammad had a powerful imagination and wanted to plant his ideas like mighty cedars. But nobody understood this. Perhaps Muhammad did not understand it himself, if I may borrow al-A'sha's words.

Now that nobody would listen to him, he became even more determined.

The whole town gossiped about Muhammad, everybody insulted him, everybody mocked him. And apart from two of his close relatives, Muhammad had not received a single reaction from his own clan.

This hurt him, and at home he discussed it with Khadija. 'I have the feeling I'm dead to them.'

The first family member to respond had been Ali, Muhammad's cousin. One evening, he dropped by and headed directly to Muhammad's room. He got straight to the point, 'Muhammad. I'll follow you blindly and I'll follow you with an open mind. You're like an older brother to me, and you've always been my example. From this moment on, I'm at your service; I'll do whatever you ask of me.'

'I wouldn't have expected anything less. Mecca needs you, Ali,' said Muhammad, and he kissed him on the forehead.

The second family member was Abu Talib, Muhammad's wealthy uncle.

Muhammad was worried about what his clan thought. Their support was crucial to him. With their backing, nobody would dare to throw a stone at him again, let alone try to kill him.

But when a response from his clan was not forthcoming, Muhammad took matters into his own hands. A sura was revealed to him:

> 'We have never destroyed a people that did not have someone who warned them.
> Take no other God besides Allah.
> Your Creator has commanded you, "Serve no one but Him!"
> Muhammad.
> Call on your nearest kinsmen.
> Accept, therefore, this pure faith, and distance yourself from the unbelievers.
> 'Trust in Him!
> The Almighty. The Forgiving One.
> Think about God when you stand up again, when you sit, and when you lie on your side.
> He hears all things. He sees all things.'

It was a major turning point for Muhammad. He could no longer bear the silent treatment he was getting from his family. They had to take a stand. Are my kinsmen with me or against me?

With this new sura he wanted to force them to decide. They were either on the side of Allah or on the side of the idols. A third possibility did not exist.

He discussed this with Khadija and invited all his male relatives to dinner at their home.

The family included very rich men, as well as others who were poor. The wealthy among them lived in splendid houses, were merchants, and members of the city council. The poor men lived in tents in the desert.

Compared to other dwellings in Mecca, Khadija's home was a palace. At the beginning of the evening, the men gathered at the door.

The head servant of the household welcomed the guests and escorted all of them to the sitting room. Among the group were two very important men.

One was Muhammad's revered old Uncle Talib. He was also Muhammad's spiritual father. He still had a stall at the Friday market in Mecca. He did not accept Muhammad's faith but supported him unconditionally.

The second man of importance was Abu Lahab, another of Muhammad's uncles. This rich merchant was a member of Mecca's Council of Elders.

Abu Lahab considered Muhammad a disgrace to the whole family. He had tried everything to dissuade him from his mission, 'Don't do this, Muhammad! Don't do this! You have reached the age of reason. Why are you always bothering my business associates with this Allah of yours? Why are you trying to force your Allah down my colleagues' throats? You must stop this or I'll have you declared insane to protect our clan from this disgrace.'

All the same, Muhammad warmly received Abu Lahab at the door and escorted him to a comfortable chair in the room. He still hoped to get the support of his powerful uncle. If he was able to convince him, it would mean a breakthrough.

Once everyone was inside, Muhammad nodded in my direction and ordered, ‘Wine!’

34 Abu Lahab, the Leader of Muhammad's Clan

Years later, Muhammad forbade wine. But now, three jugs of wine and a large number of cups were brought into the room.

Once the wine had been poured for all the guests, it was time to eat. The servants carried in large trays with an array of dishes. It was a festive meal, as one would expect in Khadija's home.

The men put out their pipes, washed their hands, and sat down to a feast. It lasted a long time. Muhammad wanted to keep the men from refilling their cups too quickly and getting drunk.

He cautiously started to chant his sura, '*Bi-smi llahi ar-rahmani ar-rahim. La 'ilaha 'illa llah*. In the name of Allah. He is love. He gives. He forgives.'

'There he goes again,' Abu Lahab muttered.

With a pointed glance, Uncle Talib urged Muhammad to keep quiet.

I, Zayd, was standing right behind Muhammad and saw his right hand trembling. His wife Khadija was listening from the hallway and whispered, 'Muhammad! Behave yourself! These men are your guests.'

I offered Muhammad a cup of water. He took a sip, turned to Abu Lahab, and said, 'Allah himself has given me the task of inviting my immediate family to follow him. Allah is One. He is all-knowing.'

'Muhammad! Just stop! I've heard this over and over again. I thought you invited me here as a sign of reconciliation, however, you have only fed us so you can fill our ears with your nonsense,' Abu Lahab snapped at him.

'Think what you want,' said Muhammad, 'but I still don't understand how a wise and great man like Abu Lahab can revere an idol, a meaningless god of stone that can't even swat a mosquito buzzing around its nose.'

Abu Lahab pushed his plate aside and said, 'You invite me to your home, only to insult me? You need to put this Allah in your past. You're an embarrassment to our clan. The only thing anybody can talk about is you. We have held our tongues until now, but I'm warning you. If you keep this up, I'm going to banish you from the clan. Then you'll be like a crazed camel who has lost his way in the desert.

'Do whatever you want,' Muhammad heatedly responded, 'Allah is great! He is the One who determines everything, not Abu Lahab.'

Ali turned toward Abu Lahab to say something, but Abu Talib admonished him with his cane to remain silent.

Then Abu Lahab hastily wiped his hands with a napkin, threw it on his plate, stood up, and exited the house. Everyone else silently followed his example.

Muhammad was now standing in the courtyard all alone, abandoned by his kinsmen.

I, Zayd, was right behind him. Khadija and Ali came and stood beside him.

'So, I can't count on my clan,' Muhammad sadly said to Khadija.

She took his hand.

'Now at least I know where I stand,' he continued, 'Abu Lahab threatened me; compared me to a crazy camel; declared me an outlaw. Now anybody can kill me without fear of reprisal from my clan. But Abu Lahab doesn't know what Muhammad is made of. I'll teach him a lesson. I'll show him what shame really feels like.'

Then Muhammad fell silent. I went to the kitchen and got him a cup of sugarcane water to calm his nerves. He took a sip, handed me the cup, and retreated to his quarters.

Muhammad was sick with grief that evening. He crawled into bed and lay there for three whole days.

I waited in the courtyard for him to open his door and come outside, but he did not venture out. On the third day, when the sun began to sink behind the date palms, I grabbed a lantern, carefully opened the door and entered his room.

He was lying sprawled on his back, with the blanket pulled over his head. I knelt beside him and whispered, 'Muhammad.'

He did not respond.

'Muhammad.'

He did not move.

I gently pulled the blanket from his face. There were beads of sweat on his forehead. He opened his eyes and said, sadly, 'What is it, Zayd?'

'Oh, nothing, I just came to read you a sura.'

He shut his eyes again and listened to me:

'By the radiant day.
And by the night in which one rests.
Muhammad! Your Creator has not abandoned you
and has not forgotten you.
The hereafter shall truly be better for you than this life.
He shall uplift you so you feel happy.

Did He not find you an orphan and give you shelter?
Did He not find you needy and give you prosperity?
Never speak harshly to the orphan.
Never turn away the beggar.
And speak with respect about the favours of your God.'

And although tears streamed down Muhammad's cheeks, his face unexpectedly broke into a smile.

35 Ali the Poet, Philosopher, and Orator

Once again, I went to visit Ali. He was now the adviser and right hand of Umar, the second Caliph. I wanted to ask him more about the night Muhammad invited his kinsmen to dinner, and Abu Lahab threatened to banish Muhammad from the clan, like one would a crazed camel.

Ali was nothing like Umar and Uthman. They were political leaders, with all the slyness and nasty practices that go hand-in-hand with that. When they ruled the new Islamic Empire, they lived like kings.

But Ali always lived a simple life. He continued to live in his old home, just like before. He was honest and pure of heart—clearly not suited to be a leader. He was more a poet and a philosopher.

Ali greatly preferred reading books to fighting on the front line. He was an orator who charmed crowds with his words. I have committed many of his proverbs to paper, so I know many of his sayings by heart. Allow me to share some of them:

'Time vanishes like a foreboding spring cloud. Seize the moment, lest you miss it.'

'Every breath you take brings you a step closer to death.'

'Those who struggle with life's little problems will be troubled with big problems.'

'Never count on two things: your health or your money.'

'Be patient! It is the remedy for sadness and longing.'

'Sweet fragrances; honey; riding one's horse; gazing at flowers, grass, and water, these are the things that will rid you of pain and sorrow.'

'There are joyous times and trying times. Do not exaggerate in the joyous times, nor be impatient when you are tested.'

'Take what life gives you. And turn away from that which you cannot have.'

'Those who search, find. That is the secret of life.'

'Happiness can be found, even in the darkest of days.'

'Whatever you are busy with, will end. And whatever will be, will be.'

I was now at Ali's door, waiting to be announced.

Yet, I still knocked before I entered.

Every time I knock on a door, I think of Muhammad. In the Qur'an he taught us how to conduct ourselves. As followers of Muhammad, we had to knock before we went inside anywhere. We used to be like camels, barging into a person's home without any warning. But Muhammad corrected us, 'Knock on the door, and if you are allowed to enter, audibly call out "Salaam!", so everybody knows you're there.'

So I knocked on the door to the courtyard.

'Enter Zayd!' Ali cried.

I entered and loudly exclaimed, 'Salaam.'

Ali received me with open arms, 'Hello my friend. Welcome my brother. What a joy to be able to embrace you again.'

He called to his wife, 'Fati, Zayd is here.'

Fati, or Fatima, was Muhammad's favourite daughter. I remember it as if it were yesterday. Muhammad simply adored her; he joked with her whenever he saw her playing in the courtyard, 'Hey Fati! Why has Allah made you so beautiful? Now, what will I do, I don't want to lose you to anybody. I want to keep you all to myself until you are old and ugly and no longer have any teeth. Only then will I give you away.'

Muhammad ultimately gave his favourite daughter to Ali. They now had two sons, Hassan and Husayn.

Fatima liked me, and whenever she ran into me somewhere, she cheerfully called, 'Zayd, you are my father's shadow. He is dead, but his shadow still moves among us.'

After she had greeted me warmly, she went back into the house. Ali escorted me outside to a comfortable wooden bench in the shade of the trees.

Two young dark-skinned servant girls appeared. One had a jug of sweet rose water in her left hand and a tray with two decorative glasses in her right hand. The other was carrying a plate heaped with ruby-red grapes, apples, and freshly-picked baby cucumbers with their yellow blossoms still attached.

After we caught up a bit about our families and children I said, 'Ali, you once told me I could always come to you if I had any questions. Can you tell me more about what happened the night the men of the family were invited to Muhammad's house, when Abu Lahab threatened him and left in a rage?'

36 The Elders of the Clan

Ali let out a deep sigh. The truth is often painful.

'Uncle Abu Lahab was the leader of our clan,' Ali said, 'he was also one of the most powerful men of Mecca and the head of the city council. In fact, he was the person who looked after the idols in the Kaaba. Abu Lahab hoped to reach an agreement with Muhammad by promising him a seat on the Council of Mecca and a substantial income. That night, he understood Muhammad couldn't be bought and couldn't be stopped. After going home angry, Abu Lahab called a gathering of the clan elders the very next day. I wasn't allowed to be there, but my father told me how it went:

"It was the middle of the night and we were all still with Abu Lahab. We had been drinking tea for hours, the teapots were empty, and the water pipes doused. But the discussion was far from over. Abu Lahab had the last word, 'When your leg is infected with the plague, you sever it from the body, otherwise the infection spreads. That is where we are—I'm cutting Muhammad off from the clan.'

"Everyone smoked; everyone contemplated. It felt like the silence lasted an eternity, so somebody needed to say something. I put out my pipe and reacted, 'Listen, Abu Lahab! I'm your brother Talib. I raised Muhammad as my own son. He's very dear to me. If we banish him from the clan, he's fair game. Anybody can take his life without fear of being avenged by our clan. Abu Lahab! You're the head of this clan. Have you carefully considered what we would do if somebody killed Muhammad? Are we to leave his body on the street for the wild dogs? You may do whatever you like, but I will not leave him there. You may choose to be silent about the death of a kinsmen, but I will choose revenge—declare war on the offender's clan. I will do this in honour of our clan.

'Brother, have you really thought this through? It hardly ever happens that someone is banished from his clan. It's a rare event, an extraordinary situation. It only occurs if there's no other solution or if the whole clan's existence is threatened. This is only something you do to prevent a war, when the enemy is powerful and wants to wipe out the women and children of your clan. Fortunately, there is no war, Abu Lahab.'

'Muhammad has declared war. A catastrophic war,' Abu Lahab shouted at me.

'It's not a war.'

'What is it, then?' Abu Lahab asked.

'I don't know, but it's not a war, and our clan isn't in danger.'

'Muhammad has declared war, but you refuse to accept it,' Abu Lahab retorted.

'No man, no woman, no child, no camel, no goat from our clan feels threatened by Muhammad. I cannot support this!' I shouted in return."

'My father rose to his feet and walked out,' said Ali. 'He heard a stir behind him and then footsteps. The elders had followed him outside.

"Isn't the night air refreshing," my father heard them remark.'

37 The Help of Angels

Ali escorted me back to the stable where I had left my horse. 'Zayd, you've seen it all yourself, you went everywhere with Muhammad, you actually know more about him than I do, so why all these questions?'

'I want your voice reflected in my book,' I said, 'what's more, I'm worried that I give my imagination too much free reign. Your voice and your father's voice will give my book a soul. Besides, I was young and not involved in everything that happened.

'Ali, you're a poet and a philosopher. I would like to include this quote of yours in my book:

"Do not stretch out your hand for something
that is unreachable.
But whereto you stretch out your hand,
shall become reachable."

'You once told me these words were inspired by Muhammad. He reached for the unreachable, the unimaginable, and achieved his aim.

'Others knew Muhammad as a prophet. You and I experienced him as a man. Ali, tell me something remarkable about the man Muhammad.'

'Zayd, you already know what I'm going to say. We knew Muhammad well. He had an incredible drive. He once said to me, "Ali, the unreachable is reachable. The more unreachable, the more reachable it is!"

'With every decision he made, he took more risks. Yet he had the ability to turn a risk into an opportunity, to make it a reliable factor.

'He fell, he fell deep, though he remained patient and rose again. He had the patience of no other man. That's why Allah calls on everyone to be patient.

'He continued to fight until he transformed his fantasy into an earthly reality.

'Muhammad was a unique being. If I'm honest, I would have to admit he was often delusional, yet he was able to achieve his objective.

'Zayd, remember when we fought together in the war? Mecca's army consisted of a few thousand men, and we were only a few hundred strong. They destroyed us, and the followers began to desert. Muhammad was left behind with just you and me. It was a lost cause. Then suddenly he cried out to his followers, "Do not flee. Allah will send help. Look up at the sky: there are hundreds of angels descending to help us."

'It was hard to comprehend how he did it. He saw the angels and continued fighting, and we fought at his side. The followers returned, and together we fought alongside the angels with all our might, and the enemy retreated. Do you remember, Zayd? That was Muhammad. He made the impossible possible.'

Ali embraced me again by the stable door and said, 'Come visit more often. My sons need their uncle Zayd.'

I promised, but fate decided otherwise—I would never see him again.

Ali eventually became the fourth Caliph. One night when he was praying in the mosque, a man named Ibn Muljam took the spot right behind him. The minute Ali was finished praying, he struck him in the middle of the head with his sword. Ali collapsed dead on the floor.

38 Slaves and Women

Ali had talked to me about Muhammad's drive, and when I read Ali's texts, I am amazed at how much faith he has in his fellow man. He literally says, 'Man can achieve anything he puts his mind to. And nothing can stop him when he focuses all his attention on achieving his objective.'

Ali made me see this. And it helped me to better understand Muhammad's life.

I mentioned earlier that Muhammad was sickened with grief after that disastrous visit with his kinsmen.

After three nights and three days, he finally got out of bed.

He grabbed a towel and headed to the date fields.

I hurried after him.

By the river that ran past the date palm trees, he undressed and jumped into the water. He could not swim; he moved like a camel. He dove under water three times, for minutes on end, and each time he came up, he loudly screeched:

'Allaaaaaaaaaaaaaaah! Help me! Allaaaaaaaaaaaaaaaaaaaah! Help me!'

It was scary.

When he came out of the water, I was afraid to approach him, but I forced myself. He grabbed the towel from me and tied it around his waist. He stood in the sun until he was dry, put on his clothing, and tossed the towel back to me.

I just stood there, waiting, because my actions were always determined by his next move. He walked toward the fields. I followed him with the wet towel slung over my shoulder.

Muhammad had changed his approach. He had needed those three long days and nights in bed to think. Now he knew what to do.

He had hoped until the very last moment that he could bring about his revolution with the help of the wealthy traders, Mecca's prominent citizens, his clan, and his influential uncle Abu Lahab.

But now he saw it differently. The hierarchy of power had to change completely. For that, he did not need to turn to the rich but to the women, who were suppressed, and to those men and women who had been humiliated to the core: the slaves. They would be the driving force behind the task Muhammad had received.

Muhammad had wanted to bathe in the river to wash off his old way of thinking, to begin with a clean slate.

Now, more convinced than ever, he went into the fields where the slaves toiled. And he sought out the women, who were constantly mistreated within the walls of their houses and in their tents.

As always, I followed him.

39 Bilal, the Free Slave

Muhammad left the city behind and spent day and night going from farm to farm.

For months on end, he talked to the slaves.

When he spoke to the women, I stood guard in front of their houses or by the entrance of their tents.

When he was talking to the slaves, I sat high up a tree. As soon as I saw a farm's foreman approaching, I warned Muhammad.

It feels like a century has passed since those days.

Sometimes I find it hard to believe that I am the one who experienced so much with Muhammad.

I was now riding through the fields outside of Mecca looking for Bilal, a former slave.

Bilal had grown old. He lived in a fine, large, stone house and had forty-three grandchildren.

Bilal once worked on a farm where vegetables were grown. What first comes to mind is his bowed back gleaming like ebony in the hot sun, and only then his face. He sang while he worked; he hummed. His voice calmed the slaves in the fields. He later devoted this same voice to Allah.

I can still see Muhammad before me, walking toward him, and how Bilal straightened his back when he saw the messenger approaching.

But I shall let Bilal tell the story in his own words, from the beginning:

'They call me Bilal. My family name is Habashi. I'm black,

as black as the night. I'm a descendant of the neighbouring Habesha people and the son of a slave. A slave dealer brought me to Mecca when I was a child. My master purchased me at Mecca's Friday bazaar. In the years that I worked for him, I grew into a strong man. He harnessed me to his plough like you would an ox, and I worked his fields. I had the yoke across my shoulders and was pulling the plough through the hard ground, when I saw Muhammad approaching. I knew who he was, I'd already heard his message, but I'd never seen him up close. A slave nearby whispered, "He's the one everybody's been talking about, the messenger."

'Although slaves were not allowed to go to the city, Muhammad's message had reached us anyway. The word had spread that he was inviting people to follow his Allah. I'd heard that, surrounded by a group of his young followers, he'd solemnly stood with his back to the Kaaba to praise his Allah.

'The slaves gossiped about him. I'd seen Muhammad before; I'd seen him talking to slaves in the dark of the night. And suddenly there he was, right in front of me.

"You have a beautiful voice!" he said.

'I said nothing, I looked around to see if the foreman had noticed him.

"From whom did you get such a voice?"

"I don't really know."

"What's your name?" He asked.

"My name is Bilal."

"Bilal Habashi, then," he said.

'Until that time I didn't have a family name. I was just called Bilal, but Muhammad gave me a family name: Habashi, Bilal of the Habesha people.

"There is only one Allah," he began while I was terrified that the foreman would see us. "Allah is the Maker of all things. All people are equal before Him. We are all brothers! In His Kingdom, there is no difference between white people, black people, or brown people."

'Other slaves were staring at me. I had grown deaf—could no longer hear him. Since these slaves were watching us, he turned to them and recited one of his newest Qur'an texts:

"Wa-sh-shams wa-dhuha-ha
Wa-l-qamar idha talaha
Labbay-ka llahumma labbay-ka
Labbay-ka la sharika la-ka labbay-ka …
By the sun and when it shines.
And by the moon when it follows.
Here I am at Your service, oh Allah, here I am.
You have no partner, here I am …"

'His words made my heart race.

"What do you want from me, Muhammad?" I said in a hushed voice.

"Your voice, Bilal. Allah didn't give you such a voice without a reason. I need you. You must come with me."

"I belong to my boss. I can't just go with you!"

"You're nobody's property. Cast off the yoke of slavery and come with me."

'Fortunately, the foreman appeared in the distance. Muhammad disappeared behind the trees.

'How could I just cast off the yoke from my shoulders and go with him? What did he need my voice for anyway? Where did he want to take me? I couldn't sleep the entire night after we spoke.

"To paradise," Muhammad said the next day.

"What paradise?"

"After death, we all return to Him. Look around you. Everything you see will die and come back to life. We're also going to die and will be brought back to life to join Him."

"Muhammad! I don't understand a word you're saying. What exactly do you want from me?" I anxiously asked.

"Divine texts are sent to me," Muhammad said, "they are revealed to me by Allah. I want you to speak his words aloud. I'll place a stool at the market. You'll stand on it and loudly recite the suras. You'll sing Allah's words, chant them."

"How, Muhammad? If I'm stuck here behind this plough."

"Cast off the iron shackle from your neck. Allah has freed you. Come with me. Don't be afraid. You're not alone. I have more and more followers among the slaves."

'It was impossible to free myself; I was born with that shackle. I didn't go with him, and every time Muhammad appeared in the fields again, I turned my back on him. And he no longer spoke to me. Six months passed. There was more and more talk about him. I heard the slaves conversing about him in the darkness. I heard the female slaves humming his words at night. Wherever I went, I heard people talking about him:

"Muhammad and his followers fought with the gatekeepers of the market."

"Yesterday, two more young slaves swore allegiance to Muhammad."

"A group of his followers sang Qur'an verses on the Kaaba Square."

"Women shout his name from behind their windows when they see him pass by."

“A group of women climbed onto a rooftop to catch an adoring glimpse of Muhammad.”

‘The landowners had prohibited their slaves from talking to him. They sent their guard dogs after Muhammad if he showed up in their fields.

‘It happened early one evening. Suddenly, I couldn’t stand the weight of that iron plough on my back. I threw it on the ground and fled barefoot into town, looking for Muhammad. When I found him, I shouted, “Allah is One and Muhammad is His messenger.”

‘Muhammad immediately put a stool on the Kaaba Square and said, “Stand on it. Chant with all your might, recite after me:

“Wa-s-sama’i wa-t-tariqi
Wa-ma ’adra-ka ma t-tariqu …
By the sky and the night star!
It is a radiant star.
Every soul is watched over.
Humankind should be aware of what they are made.
They are made of leaping fluid that runs from the back of the father to the ribs of the mother.
Indeed, He is able to call back humankind.
On the day the secrets are revealed.
By pregnant clouds filled with rain.
By the heavens from which the rain falls.
By the soil, split by a plant.
The Qur’an is a recitation, conclusive in all respects.”’

40 The Virgins

Bilal's mysterious voice was perfect for the task at hand.

Everybody and anybody who heard him, stopped to listen.

Muhammad now had a jewel among his followers, because Muhammad's own voice was monotonous and pushy. He irritated people. It was a voice fit for a fight; it was hardly inviting. He was so inspired and convinced of his own message, he sometimes stuttered and forcefully flung his arms in the air—arms that spread unrest, and created chaos in one's mind and among the citizens of Mecca.

Bilal's voice, on the other hand, was completely suited for the melodious tone of Muhammad's prose. Bilal's voice made the message more effective.

When he recited Muhammad's verses, people stopped to listen. Only now that Muhammad had relegated himself to the background, did people hear his words. They finally appreciated what he had to say and were moved by his prose.

Everybody in town was talking about that black man Bilal. The young people came to admire him. They were tired of the corruption in Mecca and the revolting customs of their ancestors. Muhammad gave them a new path to follow. He spoke of an Allah, who made ships float on the sea like leaves in the wind.

With Bilal's voice, Muhammad implored:

'Do not force a woman if she does not want to share your bed.'

'The idols serve the wealthy merchants. Only they benefit from them.'

'Men! Join me! Fight for Allah. If you die, you'll go to paradise, where virgins in green dresses await you with a jug of wine and two bowls of fruit.'

'Look at those mountains. Allah stationed them on the earth like giant pegs to prevent tremors.'

'Look at the moon. Allah suspended it as a light in the sky to illuminate your nights.'

Nobody had ever said such things. Nobody had ever heard such things.

When Bilal stopped speaking, people began discussing his words among themselves, 'Allah, the Maker of the rain. Do you actually believe it?'

'Nonsense. What Muhammad proclaims is absurd.'

'If you follow Muhammad, you're welcomed to paradise by harlots in skimpy green dresses.'

'Our gods are lifeless stone, but Muhammad's Allah is a light that burns on blessed olive oil. What a fantasy!'

Still there was strength in his message. It sounded like progress. The sheer notion of destroying stone idols, which were thousands of years old, captured the attention of the youth.

The Council of Mecca was distressed by this development. Abu Lahab saw no way out. Now that he had failed to stop Muhammad using his influence, he secretly forged a plan to eliminate him.

One day when Muhammad was with a group of his supporters on the Kaaba Square, and Bilal was reciting his verses aloud, a strange man forced his way through the crowd and struck Muhammad on the head with a stone. Muhammad fell to the ground unconscious, and the man fled.

Umar and Ali chased after the culprit. Abu Bakr and Uthman knelt beside Muhammad. They wiped the blood from his face and tried to give him a sip of water, but Muhammad just lay there like a dead man. They lifted his limp body off the ground, placed it over Bilal's shoulder, and took him home.

Rumours spread like wildfire, 'Muhammad is dead!'

'A stranger from outside Mecca wounded Muhammad with a stone.'

'Muhammad is no longer Muhammad.'

'This is the end of his Allah!'

'Muhammad is gone. He's now with his virgins in paradise!'

41 The Physician

Everybody thought Muhammad had not survived the attack: that Abu Bakr, Umar, and Uthman had buried him in secret.

But Muhammad was not dead. He lay in his bed, lifeless.

When they brought the unconscious Muhammad home, Umar locked the door from inside and ordered, 'Nobody comes in! And nobody goes out!'

I was the only one allowed to go outside, via the rooftops and over the walls.

In the middle of the night, a large stone was thrown through the window. I rushed to the roof and caught a glimpse of a few young men with stones in their hands on the street below.

Umar grabbed a stick straight away, ran outside by himself, and struck them so hard they scurried off like frightened stray dogs.

Umar was a fighting man, a man of the front line. Losing was not an option. Later he became the warlord who commanded Muhammad's army. Still later, when he became Caliph, he attacked the Persian Empire. He also chased the last Persian king all the way to the borders of Khurasan.

Once the stone throwers were gone, Umar sent me to gather Muhammad's followers, 'Ask them to come here to guard the house, or else the enemy might set it on fire.'

In the dark of night, I rode to all the addresses I knew to ask for help. Men came and stood guard until the early morning hours.

Meanwhile, Abu Bakr asked a physician to come to the house.

I, Zayd, must lay down my pen for a moment and close my eyes so I can picture the night that physician treated Muhammad. I can see Muhammad in bed with his eyes shut and his chest slowly heaving.

Abu Bakr was kneeling on his right knee, holding a lantern so the physician could stitch up Muhammad's wound with a needle.

I was in the doorway, keeping an eye on every movement in the room as well as in the courtyard.

Uthman had Muhammad's wrist in his hand and quietly gave his heart rate to the physician.

Umar was kneeling at the foot of the bed massaging Muhammad's feet to keep his blood circulating.

'More clean rags,' the physician ordered.

I hurried to the servants, 'Bring clean rags.'

'How is Muhammad?' the old black servant asked.

I did not answer.

The physician examined Muhammad once again and showed us how to clean and dress the wound. When the doctor left, Abu Bakr went to the other side of the courtyard, to Khadija's room, to tell her that Muhammad seemed a bit better.

At dawn the next day, Muhammad opened his eyes.

I was the first one to witness this. There are no words to describe my joy.

42 A Defiant Muhammad

Muhammad stayed in bed for ten days. Then he got up and started to pace around the courtyard. He had grown thin.

The old servant of the household spoiled him with hearty meals. To give him strength, she made him revitalizing drinks by mixing date syrup with the milk of young camels. She also stuck brown seeds from desert plants in dried figs, placed these on a plate, poured honey over them, and served this to him with a cup of freshly brewed tea when he was resting in the shadow of the courtyard wall.

In the afternoon, when the sun disappeared behind the walls of the house and the heat retreated, she made a wood fire and grilled goat balls for Muhammad. She seasoned them with fragrant herbs, salt, pepper, and some slices of fresh lemon. The delicious smell of roasting meat drifted over the walls into the street. This was how people knew that all was well in Muhammad's house.

Khadija smiled again, and although she had grown old, she cheerfully ran up-and-down the stairs like a much younger woman.

Nobody in the city really knew how Muhammad was doing. They knew he was still alive, but they thought he would never be the same. Abu Bakr, Umar, and Uthman came by a few times a day, but they did not talk much with him and did not tell him what was happening on the street. His physician had ordered him to rest for at least another week.

But Abu Bakr, Umar, and Uthman had not wasted any time. They thoroughly investigated who was behind the attack. The man who tried to kill Muhammad was a thug hired by one of Abu Lahab's accomplices. A servant of Abu Lahab's wife had paid the young men who had thrown stones at Muhammad's window.

The healing period was coming to an end. Muhammad was feeling much better and appeared more defiant than ever.

'Zayd,' he called. 'Clean up this room. Get rid of this sickbed. I want it out of my sight.'

I, Zayd, was not about to clean up anything. I had not been an errand boy for the longest time. I was the one who made sure the messenger's wishes were fulfilled.

So I summoned the servants and repeated, 'Clean up this room. Get rid of the bed.'

And I opened the windows to the courtyard to air out his room.

I saw Abu Bakr, Umar, and Uthman talking to one another by the front door.

'I want to meet in my quarters. Show them in!' Muhammad said.

I asked them inside, and they entered, all smiles. They kissed Muhammad on his forehead, on his face and hands, and then the four of them sat down in a circle on the floor.

I shut the windows.

Muhammad was the messenger!

Abu Bakr succeeded him and as first Caliph united the realm with his wisdom.

Umar made Islam known all over the world.

I, Zayd, collected Muhammad's ideas and compiled a miraculous book—the Qur'an.

And Uthman compelled the world to read the Qur'an.

43 The Turning of the Tide

The next day when I was by the courtyard well, I noticed Muhammad was restless. He was pacing, and I could see he was trembling; he had no control over his legs. I immediately knew he was receiving a new message from Allah—soon a sura would be revealed to him.

He was shaking his head, mumbling, and uttering broken sentences:

'Tabbat yada … tabbat yada
Abu Lahab wa-tabba
Ma aghna … 'an-hu
Malu-hu … wa-ma kasaba.'

At moments like these, I did not dare get too close to him. I listened attentively. I could not always hear what he was saying; sometimes I caught a few words:

'Tabbat yada … wa-tabba …
Ruined … Abu Lahab
Perish … perish …
Possessions … not benefit him …
Blazing fire … rope … fibres.'

Drenched in sweat, exhausted, he leaned against the wall for support.

I ran to the bedroom, grabbed a sheet, ran back, and threw the sheet around his shoulders. I led him by the arm to his room. I placed a pillow under his head and told him to lie down for a while.

Then I quietly closed the door and stood guard outside.

It would most likely be clear tomorrow which sura had been revealed to him.

The next day, Muhammad's mission got yet another boost. The people of Mecca still had no clue about what was going to happen.

Abu Bakr, Umar, and Uthman arrived earlier than usual to visit and talked with one another behind closed doors. I had to go to the market to pick up Muhammad's shoes. When I returned, Umar called to me.

He whispered, 'Hurry! Assemble the men on the Council Square, right in front of Abu Lahab's office. And stay with them! Wait there!'

On my trusted horse, I galloped to the place where our orator Bilal Habashi was hiding from his owner.

'Go to the Council Square,' I instructed, and I continued on my way to notify the other followers.

The sun was high in the sky when we gathered with seventy-three men on the square across from Abu Lahab's office. People looked on curiously. We also did not know what was going to happen next. We caught a few glimpses of Abu Lahab behind the partially drawn curtains.

At a certain moment, Muhammad came striding onto the square with Abu Bakr to his right, Umar to his left, and Uthman behind him.

Everybody looked at Muhammad in surprise. The people on the square made way for him. Nobody had expected this. Everybody thought his days were done, but Muhammad held his shoulders high, displaying more resolve than ever to his followers.

Bilal exclaimed:

'La 'ilaha 'illa llah
Muhammadan rasulu llah.'

The followers cried out all together:

'There is only one God: Allah
And Muhammad is His messenger.'

Umar placed the stool on its spot. Muhammad mounted it, pointed his finger at Abu Lahab's window and shouted:

'Tabbat yada Abu Lahab wa-tabba …
Ruined are the hands of Abu Lahab.
May he himself also perish.
His possessions and his deeds shall not benefit him.
He shall be brought to a blazing fire.
His wife likewise, she who carries wood for the fire.
With a rope around her neck, woven from the fibres of a date palm.'

Umar picked up a stone and threw it through Abu Lahab's window.

That day a shock went through the crowd in Mecca. Muhammad had struck the heart of power with an arrow from his bow.

44 The Followers

Muhammad now needed constant protection.

Abu Bakr came up with the idea.

Uthman gave it shape.

Umar implemented the plan.

Some of Muhammad's strapping followers guarded his house day and night. Umar also made it clear to Muhammad that he was no longer allowed go out on his own.

Umar took me aside and said, 'Listen, Zayd, Muhammad shouldn't go anywhere by himself. I'm holding you responsible if he does. Understood?'

'Understood,' I said.

During their next meeting, Uthman spoke first, 'The city is on edge. Everyone is waiting for our next move.'

Umar said, 'The time has come to focus on the entire population.'

Abu Bakr said, 'The Council has lost face. Now that we've damaged Abu Lahab's reputation, they'll retaliate with violence.'

Muhammad was quiet and listened.

'What do you think, Muhammad?' Uthman asked.

'You're right, Uthman,' Muhammad replied, 'the city is awaiting our next move. We have entered a new phase. The time of orating from a stool is over. We must convince the entire population. We must devise plans to take possession of the Kaaba. We don't know when this will be possible—only Allah knows that. We've taken the first step. Now we must take the next one!'

I went to fetch some rose water and fruit.

When I returned, the men were strolling in the courtyard. I placed the jug of sweet water and a bowl of fruit on the bench under the old tree.

I had to miss the second half of the meeting because Muhammad insisted I visit Bilal. His owner had discovered Bilal's hiding place and sent men to beat him up. Afterwards, they nailed him to the ground in the scorching sun. An entire day passed before one of his friends rescued him.

Khadija had filled a basket for Bilal with fruit, juice, salted meat, dried figs, camel cheese, nuts, a new shirt, and a new pair of shoes. I took the basket and rode to Bilal to deliver Muhammad's message: 'Do not weep, Bilal. Allah has seen you!'

The violence increased. Not only was Bilal almost beaten to death; the Council had hired a gang of thugs who, under cover of darkness, broke into the homes of Muhammad's followers, seriously injured them, and ransacked their houses, destroying everything.

Muhammad's followers complained, but each time he said, 'Be patient!' They pressured Muhammad for permission to defend themselves using force, but Muhammad advised against it, 'Show patience. I have not received a command from Allah allowing the use of violence.'

But Umar had run out of patience. He raised his voice, 'This can't go on any longer, Muhammad. Stop being so weak! You're not Isa, who turned the other cheek when a blow was delivered. Make a decision. Give us a new message.

'When they lift a hand against us, we must strike back hard!'

The burden weighing on Muhammad's shoulders grew. I saw him pacing in the courtyard, deep in thought, with his hands clasped behind his back.

45 Uncle Talib's Warning

Late one night, there was a knock at the door. I took the torch and peered through the small hatchway. It was Uncle Talib, Ali's father.

I informed Muhammad first, then escorted Talib inside. I knew it was urgent. Otherwise he would not have come in the middle of the night.

Muhammad embraced him, and they sat down straight away.

I fetched a jug of water and two cups and knelt on the floor behind Muhammad. I watched and listened.

'Muhammad, I'm like a father to you,' Talib said, 'I beg you. Talk to Abu Lahab. They will finish you off, and I'm no longer in a position to protect you. Let's go to Abu Lahab together, first thing tomorrow, before it's too late.'

'Is this what you came to tell me? So now you've spoken, and I've heard you,' Muhammad said.

'Listen my son. There are evil plots in the making. That's why I came right away. Let me say it again, Muhammad, I can't protect you anymore. Talk to Abu Lahab.'

'This is not according to Allah's plan, he has another plan,' Muhammad said.

'What plan?' Talib asked, worried.

'It will all be clear tomorrow morning,' Muhammad said

Then he kissed his uncle's hand and accompanied him outside. Muhammad wanted to take a short stroll in the night air, but I stopped him, 'Umar has prohibited this. You must stay inside. I'll go with Uncle Talib.'

Muhammad went back into the house, and I walked with Talib as far as the market square.

Back home, I securely locked the courtyard gate behind me and was headed to my room, when I heard Muhammad call my name.

I looked around; he was standing in the dark next to the well. I walked over to him. He whispered, 'Quickly! Go to Bilal and tell him, "Early in the morning, before the sun rises, assemble your men on the market square. We are going to climb Mount Safa."'

I rode out of town, to the place where Bilal lived with Muhammad's follower Yasir. I did not ask Bilal how he was doing; I did not ask if he was available; I did not ask him if his wounds had healed; that was not my task, I was just a courier. I jumped off my horse, ran inside, embraced Bilal, and whispered the same words in his ear that Muhammad had whispered in mine, 'Early in the morning, before the sun rises, assemble your men on the market square. We are going to climb Mount Safa.'

Then I galloped home at breakneck speed.

46 The New Followers

I climbed up on the roof at dawn to keep an eye out for Abu Bakr, Umar, and Uthman. As soon as I saw the silhouettes of three riders in the distance, I called to Muhammad, 'They're coming!'

I rushed downstairs to fetch Muhammad's horse from the stable.

Muhammad took a sip of water from the bucket hanging on the well and dumped the rest into the hole in the ground the horses drank from. I handed him the reins. When the horse had finished drinking, we exited the courtyard to find Abu Bakr, Umar, and Uthman waiting.

Before setting out, I had seen that Muhammad was wearing new clothing and new shoes. I always adjusted my attire to his. Thus, I quickly put on my new shoes as well.

Muhammad had once bought them for me as a gift. Most Arabs wore shoes made of camel hide, which felt stiff to the touch, but Muhammad wore shoes made of cowhide, just like the Persians. His shoes were sturdy and elegant, and you could protect the leather by rubbing it with a creamy black paste.

I always polished Muhammad's shoes and was very fond of his footwear. One time, on his way home from a long trip, he had purchased this pair of Persian cowhide shoes for me at the market in Hijaz, but they were a few sizes too big.

'They are not for now,' Muhammad said, 'but for later, when you become a man.'

They finally fit me that year. They were elegant fawn-coloured shoes. I actually thought it was a shame to walk around in them, so I only wore them when I travelled by horse.

The first time Muhammad saw me wearing them he joked, 'Zayd, take off those shoes! Otherwise, the stray dogs of Mecca will sink their teeth into you, mistaking you for a Persian cow.'

Now, I was wearing my new shoes, riding behind Muhammad, Abu Bakr, Umar, and Uthman. Without exchanging a single word, they headed toward the market square where Bilal and the other followers were waiting for them.

As we approached the square, I could hear the men in the distance. The group was growing: a lot of young slaves and young Arabs, as well as some men from Muhammad's own clan. These were men whose hearts had been touched by Muhammad's message. There were also rebels who were sick and tired of the old authority.

Muhammad knew exactly what he was doing, but his followers were embarking on an adventure. They did not know what the next step would be or where it would take them.

There were also many people who wanted to join Muhammad's movement but still did not dare.

Muhammad had many secret followers, especially among the women of Mecca, but they did not know how to support him. Throughout all of Arab history, nobody had ever mentioned women. They were next to nothing, and men were ashamed of their daughters.

Muhammad proclaimed, 'Stop! Stop humiliating women! Paradise lies at the feet of mothers.'

And the women heard him.

But there was still a long way to go before women and particularly the female slaves could openly support Muhammad.

By now, around seventy-five men had gathered on the square. I could hear their muffled voices and make out the figure of Bilal.

'Fetch Bilal!' Muhammad ordered.

I did as told. Muhammad dismounted his horse, shook Bilal's hand, and gave him some instructions.

Then he approached his other supporters and proceeded to shake everyone's hand, *'As-salamu 'alay-kum. La 'ilaha 'illa llah.'*

He left his followers with Bilal and went off with Abu Bakr, Umar, and Uthman to Mount Safa.

'Best you stay by Bilal's side,' Muhammad said to me.

So I stayed.

47 The Meccans

We were all waiting on the market square, but I did not have a clue why.

I kept a close eye on Bilal. At one point, he called the group together. They gathered around him. Bilal said something to them I could not hear. Then the men looked up at the sky. They repeated this action a few times. I thought something might appear from the sky, that Muhammad's angels would descend, or that Allah would reveal himself this early morning, but I was wrong. They were waiting for the sun, for the first rays. And they were waiting until people were awake and had left their homes to go to work.

Moments later, the first glint of sunlight pierced the sky. People filled the streets, but only when I saw them heading toward the Kaaba Square with goats and dishes of food did I realize that today was a sacrificial feast—the holy Friday, when all the shops were closed, and people brought their offerings to the great idol al-'Uzza in the Kaaba.

Suddenly Bilal turned to the people who were passing by and cried out with all his might:

'*Ya Sabaha! Ya Sabaha!*

'Citizens of Mecca!

'The messenger Muhammad calls every one of you to Mount Safa.'

Then Bilal and the other followers made their way through the crowd, in the direction of the Kaaba, while they were all shouting:

'Allah, Allah.

'La 'ilaha 'illa llah.

'Come with us to Mount Safa!'

I was shocked by this unexpected action and trembled with excitement. Surprised, the people stepped aside with their goats and stared at Muhammad's followers as they recited their melodic Qur'an texts.

But I did not understand why they kept shouting *'Ya Sabaha! Ya Sabaha!'* These were words you only uttered when the city was in imminent danger or when an enemy was about to attack at dawn.

The people looked at one another, confused, *'Ya Sabaha?* Mount Safa?'

Mecca was teeming with energy from this strategic move by Muhammad. It was a confusing warning. Everybody knew that war was forbidden during the sacrificial feast. All the clans who fought against one another during the year laid down their arms during this feast so they could peacefully offer sacrifices to their idols. What was Muhammad trying to say with this message? For which enemy was he warning the people of the city?

He could not have come up with a better day to invite the Meccans to go to Mount Safa.

It was an action against the age-old tradition that demanded peace—an action that stirred everyone's curiosity, 'Let's go to Mount Safa and see what Muhammad has to say.'

Even the slaves were allowed to enter the city freely that day, just like ordinary citizens.

Dogs barked, donkeys stepped aside, goats bleated loudly, roosters jumped over walls, children ran after the followers, shouting, *'Ya Sabaha! Ya Sabaha!'* The women hurried outside, and the slaves, who had waited a long time to get a first-hand look at Muhammad, all headed for Mount Safa.

48 Muhammad on Mount Safa

Hundreds of people made the climb. Muhammad was all the way at the top, speaking to them through a copper bullhorn.

It was light now, so I could see everything much better. Muhammad was wearing a long Arabian shirt but without a cotton cloth wrapped around his head. His hair hung loose, it was long, down to his shoulders. It was still black, though his beard had turned grey. Now, standing there high above us, he radiated even more power and looked like a real prophet.

He turned to the people.

'Citizens of Mecca! If I were to tell you that behind this mountain lurks an army that wants to invade the city, would you believe me or not?'

Nobody responded; everybody just stared at him in silence.

'I implore you on behalf of Allah.

'All of you:

'The clan of Abdul-Muttalib!

'The Abd Manaf clan!

'The Banu Zuhrah clan!

'The Banu Tamim clan!

'The Banu Makhzum clan!

'The Banu Asad clan!

'Hear me!

'Allah has ordered me to warn you that a severe punishment awaits you.

'Swear off your idols and serve Allah.

'Say, *"La 'ilaha 'illa llah ..."*

'I ask only this of you. I ask nothing more.

‘I am simply a messenger.

‘Allah has instructed me to call you together to say, “A mighty army, Allah’s army, is behind this mountain ready to punish you for how you treat your slaves, how you treat your women, how you treat your newborn daughters.”

‘Allah wants to tell you, “Your idols are weak, nothing but powerless stones. Turn your backs on them. With Allah’s support, I will smash them to bits with a hammer and dispose of them. Then I will sweep the floor of the Kaaba clean for Allah.”’

Pandemonium broke out on the mountainside. In the history of the Arab world, nobody had ever uttered such harsh, insulting words about the idols in public. How dare Muhammad speak so rudely about the ancient gods of their ancestors!

Some people were furious—ready to assault Muhammad, but that was forbidden.

After all, it was the day of the sacrificial feast and no fighting was allowed.

The young people were enjoying all the excitement—their eyes glittered with hope because of Muhammad’s uplifting words, ‘Abandon your graven images! Turn to Allah, the Maker of the apple!’

There was much debate. Some found it deception; others thought Muhammad had indeed become a threat. And still others felt relieved.

Hope sparkled in the eyes of the slaves. ‘Oh, what a day!’ they exclaimed.

Suddenly a group of security guards on mules appeared. They drew their swords and went looking for Muhammad. ‘Shame on you! Today is the sacrificial feast,’ the women cried. But Abu Lahab had ordered the guards to arrest Muhammad for causing such a commotion during the holy festival.

They could not find him because Umar had immediately taken him to a safe place by horse.

49 The Linguist al-Jahiz

By now, Muhammad had produced a significant body of texts, and he was still coming up with new suras.

His followers learned his prose by heart, carved the verses in wood and camel bones, and wherever they went, they carried his words with them.

Women and slaves accepted these Qur'an texts as the words of Allah—words straight from heaven—but poets and scholars felt differently about Muhammad's 'fantasies'. The established poets of Mecca initially wanted nothing to do with Muhammad. But now that he, surrounded by his followers, turned up everywhere in the city and stood on a stool each time to reveal a new passage, these poets felt increasingly pressured to express their opinions about Muhammad's Qur'an texts:

'Not bad.'

'Incoherent language.'

'He isn't writing poetry; he's busy with politics.'

'He's a thief. He commits plagiarism—steals the stories of the Torah.'

'He's the prophet of women, but he deceives them.'

While I myself was grappling with his Qur'an texts, I discovered something rather curious. Muhammad could come up with commanding sentences, and people found his words thrilling, but his thinking was chaotic. He could not structure his tales. That is what I did while I was transcribing his Qur'an. Muhammad could not think chronologically. His mind always jumped from one topic to another.

That made my task easier. Nobody knows anything about my method of working. May Allah reward His servant Zayd for his disciplined approach.

During a poetry night in the desert, I fell into a conversation with the linguist al-Jahiz. We went for a walk under a dark blue sky awash with stars. I mentioned the chaos in Muhammad's texts. Al-Jahiz said something that had never occurred to me. When he elaborated on his brilliant insights about this matter, I felt humbled.

'Zayd, you're mistaken,' al-Jahiz said, 'I don't see chaos in his words; I see a new trend in the Arabic language. I compare his prose to bunches of dates hanging high in the trees. Muhammad recounts something but interrupts his story midway and moves on to something else, just like a bunch of dates branches off but stays complete nonetheless, and forms a unity.'

I had not expected an explanation like this and asked, 'What do you mean by complete and a unity? Perhaps you could give me an example?'

Al-Jahiz thought for a moment and said, 'Consider the chapter entitled "The Table". He starts with livestock, then moves on to the Trinity, then speaks about wine, then talks about gambling, then turns his attention to Maryam, then settles scores with the Jews, then enters paradise and makes his way into hell, only to return to the table, to Isa. Each story is a sprig of a bunch.'

I was awestruck and could only remain silent.

50 Adnan El Maki, the Bookbinder

I recently met a poet named Adnan El Maki, a man of around forty. I had heard him speak at a poets' circle in Mecca. He criticized the Qur'an in subtle ways. I could see he had more to say on the subject but was reluctant to do so in public. I waited for the right moment to look him up. I found him behind the counter of a bookbindery. It was his own business, where he employed about fifty men who inscribed texts on parchment, decorated them, and did the cutting work.

El Maki recognized me from the poets' gathering, but he did not actually know who I was. I tied the reins of my horse to the tree next to his shop and went to greet him.

At first he thought I was there to place an order, but I said that I had found his speech fascinating. I asked him if he would join me for lunch at the market.

'Do you mind me asking who is inviting me?' El Maki said.

'My name is Zayd, and I write.'

'What do you write about, Zayd?'

'I'm the compiler of the Qur'an; the chronicler of Muhammad.'

When he heard this, he reacted like he had been struck by lightning. He numbly stared at me as if he was made of stone. We did not exchange another word. He put on his coat, and we went off to eat something together. There was somehow a feeling of trust, as if we were old friends.

We found a spot on a bench under the old tree at the Olive Grove Eatery.

After some small talk, he said, 'I have a fundamental problem with the Allah in Muhammad's Qur'an. He bothers me. He's constantly talking about himself. Allah is egotistic; he's a self-centred Creator. He constantly wants to be praised: "Bless *Me*! Bow to *Me*! Worship *Me* day and night! Kneel before *Me*! Beg *Me*! If you don't, I'll burn you! I'll pour molten copper over you!" He's so demanding of attention, it seems like He's been robbed of it for centuries. With Him it's always *Me*, *Me*, *Me*, and *Me* again. And He just doesn't stop.'

I did not respond to his assertions. That was not my task. I was there to find out what people thought about Muhammad and to commit this to paper. I liked El Maki, and I smiled when he spoke candidly about Allah and Muhammad.

'The Allah of Muhammad claims everywhere in the Qur'an that He created humankind in a hurry. He stresses that His being is weak. He admits that His beloved creation is vulnerable and limited. Still, He takes revenge on humankind when they are unable to comprehend a difficult concept such as "Allah".

'He places his humans in an inhumane situation. He sends Muhammad as His messenger, yet gives him no proof, no miracle. And He still expects everybody to accept His messenger. Why has He made it so difficult for Muhammad? With a bit of proof, all that unrest wouldn't have been necessary.

'Oh, oh, oh, how I despise His threats. Especially His hell where people burn; where they're hung upside down. While He is the One who made humankind so weak.'

I had a pleasant lunch with El Maki. Unlike many other people, he had actually read the Qur'an—read it thoroughly.

'I liked Muhammad when he was alive,' El Maki continued, 'and now that he's dead, the feeling is even stronger. I admire him for his imagination. But the question still remains: how was it possible for him to change the world with so many strange ideas? He claimed he was a messenger in line with the prophets Ibrahim, Isma'il, Musa and Isa. He claimed that the God of Isa and Allah are one and the same, but he knew this wasn't true.

'Muhammad was sickened by those priests making the sign of the cross.

'Allah immediately dismissed the notion of the Holy Trinity.

'The Qur'an states a thousand times, "Allah is One. He was not fathered, nor does he father." Thus Allah has no son. Whoever claims otherwise gets molten iron poured down their throat. Muhammad is an earthly prophet—a beautiful being, who is the messenger of his self-made Allah.

'Muhammad is tough like leather, seared by the harsh sun.

'He says, "If you are struck, hit back with all your might!"

'Muhammad loves women, especially young women, while Isa rarely expresses a desire for women. It is doubtful whether he ever kissed a woman, but Muhammad has a voracious appetite for women. He is a connoisseur who enjoys life, while Isa suffers.

'Allah is ashamed of Maryam. How could she suddenly get pregnant out of nowhere? I have to laugh when I read the sura "Maryam": Allah sending Jabra'il to earth as a handsome young man to correct God's error. Jabra'il seducing Maryam behind the date palms and getting her pregnant.

'The God of Isa has nothing to do with Allah.

'His God allows this passage in the Old Testament:

"How beautiful you are, my love …
Your eyes are doves behind your veil.

Your teeth are like a flock of shorn ewes.
Your lips are like a crimson thread.
Your two breasts are like two fawns … that feed among the lilies."

'Exquisite. Still, Allah would tear out this page, crumple it up, and toss it, "Obscenities!"'

What a pleasure it was to eat with the poet Adnan El Maki that afternoon under an old olive tree.

51 Hasan bin Hadi, the Astronomer

It is not that I only sought out Muhammad's admirers. I also spoke to people who had completely different opinions about him, his Qur'an, and his Allah. Some saw Muhammad as a liar; others found him highly imaginative.

I went to visit the astronomer Hasan bin Hadi bin Ibrahim. He lived on the outskirts of Mecca in an unusual building with a dark blue dome, which symbolized the roof of the heavens. There, surrounded by his students, he studied the sun, the moon, and the stars.

He was cautious with his words but at the same time courageous, 'I'm not saying Muhammad lied. He didn't know any better. And that was also reflected in his Allah. Muhammad didn't understand the workings of the world. What he said was incorrect.

'I don't always understand the workings of the world either, but then I keep my mouth shut. I observe and listen.

'Muhammad spoke with such conviction about the sun, the moon, and the shadows. But he was mistaken. He thought the shadows bowed before Allah. Wrong. He couldn't see the connection between the sun, the tree, and its shadow. He saw them as unrelated elements. Incorrect. While in the stories he tells, he constantly hammers away: "Allah is all-knowing."

'But Muhammad's Allah is unknowing!

'He says: "Heaven is supported by pillars."

'How did he come to that conclusion? Which pillars? Why haven't my pupils come across these pillars in their observations? Again incorrect. Zayd, your master was ignorant—and his Allah too.'

As I went to fetch my horse from the stable, I heard Hasan bin Hadi call my name, 'Zayd! Yet, I still admire your master! It's a miracle that with such a lack of knowledge he still produced a Book capable of changing the map of the world.'

52 Talha, the Blacksmith

In the sixth year of his mission, Muhammad provoked the first real confrontation. The Council of Mecca then saw that he posed a severe threat. Whenever the security forces came across Muhammad's followers, they beat them severely.

Particularly slaves were victims of this new wave of violence. If the security guards heard that a slave had fled his owner's farm and joined Muhammad, they hunted him down and dealt with him harshly.

The streets of Mecca became a battleground for the confrontations between the security forces and Muhammad's followers. The guards hit them with their long sticks. But Muhammad still had not given his followers permission to strike back. They were only allowed to defend themselves with their bare hands.

In order to describe that turbulent period accurately, I went looking for Talha. He was the person who devised a plan to protect Muhammad's followers against the violence. Talha was a talented, young Arab, smart and cunning. After the action on Mount Safa, his true qualities emerged. Later, in Medina, he became one of the greatest warlords of the Islamic army.

I can still remember exactly what happened the day he joined Muhammad. It was a quarter of a century ago.

There was a knock. I peeked through the hatch in the door. Standing there was a handsome young man with dark eyes, neatly combed hair, a fine cotton jacket, and a dagger tucked inside his belt.

'My name is Talha. I've come to see Muhammad the messenger.'

At first, I did not recognize him, but then I realized it was the blacksmith Talha.

'Please just wait a moment,' I said.

I hurried to Muhammad's quarters: 'Talha is at the door.'

'Which Talha?'

'Mecca's famous blacksmith, Talha.'

'What does he want?'

'He says he wants to talk to the messenger.'

'Well,' Muhammad smiled, 'show him in.'

I escorted Talha inside. Muhammad cheerfully stuck out his hand and said, 'Talha the blacksmith, the man who is going to shoe the thousands of hooves of our horses in the years to come.'

Talha silently bowed his head and cupped Muhammad's hand with his powerful grip.

'Tea!' Muhammad called out.

I rushed to the kitchen and gave orders to the head servant, 'Two teas in gold-rimmed glasses. And a plate of fresh dates served on a silver tray.'

I brought the tea to the room myself. And as custom would have it, I first served our guest. I placed Muhammad's tea glass on his table and silently stood behind him at a distance.

Talha had often heard Muhammad speak on the market and had copies of his texts at home.

'I can't sleep anymore,' Talha said, 'someone is constantly repeating your words in my head.'

And he recited a short text:

'When the sun grows dark.
When the stars go out.
When the mountains begin to move.
When the heavily pregnant and cherished camels are abandoned.
When the wild animals are assembled.
When the seas seethe and swell …
When the girls are asked for which sin they were buried alive.
When the heavens are torn asunder …
I swear by the recurring stars, which finish their course and go down.
And by night when it disappears.
And by the morning when it appears.
These are the words of an outstanding messenger …
No, Muhammad is not mad.'

Then Talha knelt in front of Muhammad and said, 'I bear witness that Muhammad is an outstanding messenger.'

Thus, Talha joined Muhammad and became one of his most important followers. He was the man who made everything possible—nothing more, nothing less. I decided to go look for Talha to hear what he had to say about Muhammad.

53 An Upheaval in the Kaaba

Talha received me at home. He had grown old. He no longer fought on the front but had become the most important military adviser of Uthman, the third Caliph.

His house was like a castle, and he went everywhere in a carriage drawn by four horses, which gleamed like an enormous chunk of gold in the bright Meccan sunlight. He was always accompanied by a cavalcade of royal horsemen that rode ahead of his carriage while other horsemen took up the rear.

The captain of his house guard escorted me inside.

Talha opened his arms to embrace me, 'Zayd! Old friend. What a joy to see you. To what do I owe this unexpected visit?'

'Muhammad has departed this life. But I'm still here,' I said. 'And before I follow him, there's still something important I must do.'

'Tell me everything,' he said as he escorted me to his private quarters and offered me a spot on a bench strewn with pillows. The servant brought us fruit, sweets, and something to drink.

'Talha, can you still remember what happened when you left your blacksmith's shop and joined Muhammad's movement?'

'It was an unforgettable time. I was young, enthusiastic, and searching. Muhammad was like a torch burning in the night. I had been captivated by his tales for the longest time,' Talha said. 'Muhammad's words kept me from doing my work. I put aside my forging hammer and sought him out. After that first meeting, I spoke to him in private. He said, "Our followers are extremely vulnerable; all the violence has made them afraid. Especially the slaves are fearful of retaliations against their families. Our public actions need to be handled differently. We need a few fast men who can strike like lightning and get away quickly. These actions need to happen at important places, and swiftly, so the security guards can't get their hands on them. Do you think you can arrange this?"

'I thought for a moment and then replied, "I'll take care of it."

'That's how I became the leader of twelve men, and together we came up with different plans. For our first action, I chose the Kaaba. Except for worshipping their idols, no guard was allowed to step foot there.

'I discussed the idea with Muhammad beforehand, and he'd smiled approvingly.

'We chose a Friday afternoon because people usually went to the Kaaba then.

'We, my twelve men and I, wore lightweight camel-skin slippers and baggy white pants. One by one, we discretely entered the Kaaba. Ever since my childhood, I'd accompanied my father and brought our offerings: slaughtered goats, food, spices, gold, and fine fabric. We would burn candles and kneel before our clan's idol. It was always very busy, and there was always that wonderful smell of sacred herbs. Members of several other clans chanted softly before their own idols. I was always incredibly impressed. Particularly by the large idols adorned with gold, pearls, and satin. Now that I was inside with my men, I suddenly saw everything differently. I called my group together and without any warning, we started to recite a short sura from the Qur'an:

"Qul, huwa llahu 'ahadun
Allahu samadun

Lam yalud
Wa-lam yalid
Wa-lam …
Say, 'Allah is One.
Allah is the Eternal.
He was not fathered, nor does he father.
And there is no one equal to Him.'"

'And then we immediately dispersed among the crowd. Everybody was shocked by this swift action, which had broken the sacred silence in the Kaaba.

'People hadn't even recovered from the shock when we reassembled and loudly recited in unison:

"*Ar-rahmani ar-rahim,*
Maliki yawmi d-din …
Allah is great.
Allah is forgiving.
Allah is the true King of the universe.
Allah is the Maker of the stars."

'Nobody knew what to do. Since time immemorial, since the days when the prophet Ibrahim had laid the first cornerstone of the Kaaba, nobody had spoken aloud in the Kaaba. Something had happened that people could not comprehend. They stared at one another dismayed. And not a single security guard dared to enter the holy place.

'Next, we carried out another action and disappeared one by one, before anybody could figure out who we were.

'The news shook Mecca to the core: "Muhammad's men proclaimed the name of 'Allah' in the Kaaba."'

54 Sharpened Sticks

'This new approach worked well and it appealed to the young people,' said Talha, 'but at the same time, it provoked the city leaders. They reacted like beasts under attack.

'Muhammad was no longer the Muhammad of the past. He dared to push aside his gentle melancholic words and spoke harshly. Surrounded by his supporters, he held fiery speeches against the city's rulers and urged people to revolt. There was only one problem; Muhammad still doubted if weapons were absolutely necessary.

'So I went to talk to Umar, "Muhammad must give us permission to strike back hard, or he will lose his supporters. Our defensive approach is no longer working; the violence is now destroying us from within. Our followers are so incensed about the security guards and hired thugs who attack us, they can no longer function."

'Umar answered, "I know. I've also said this to him, but we must be patient. Muhammad has not yet received Allah's permission to use violence. Patience. Try to be patient."

'Deep in his heart Muhammad still hoped he could peacefully rid the Kaaba of its idols and transform it into the House of Allah.

'But then something else happened. Two days after my conversation with Umar, we were called together on the Kaaba Square. Muhammad climbed up on the stool. He calmly gazed at his followers and then pointed his finger at the city council's window and called out, "Last night a new message was revealed to me. Allah has granted me permission to hit back hard. You have been warned. From this day forward, I will strike with all my might."

'Umar appeared with three camels laden with sharpened sticks.

'I helped him unload the weapons. Then Muhammad handed everyone a stick. In an instance, a metamorphosis took place. The innocent followers of Muhammad became an armed militia. This served as the foundation of Muhammad's army.

'We had entered a new phase. The streets of Mecca were the scene of heavy fighting between Muhammad's militias and the security guards, backed by hired thugs. Muhammad's followers fought back fearlessly.

'Those were unforgettable days and nights. With all his might, Muhammad mercilessly struck the captain of the guards on the back with a stick, and Umar chased down the thugs.

'Decisive days, beautiful days—we felt like we were busy bringing down the hierarchy of power in Mecca.

'It was cause for thought in Mecca, and Muhammad's group of supporters grew by the day.'

When Talha and I had finished talking, we took a long walk in his garden. This was no ordinary garden. An earthly paradise had been created for Talha here, undoubtedly inspired by Muhammad's texts. As we strolled together in the shade of the trees, alongside the fragrant flowerbeds, these verses of the Qur'an came to mind:

> 'The forerunners shall be brought to the gardens of happiness, where they shall sit opposite one another on couches encrusted with jewels.

Young men who never age shall go around with jugs and cups of wine drawn from a flowing spring.
This wine shall not pain their heads or intoxicate them.
And fruit shall be brought, from which they are free to choose what they desire.
And the flesh of birds, whatever their desire.
And wholesome maidens with beautiful, dark, and expressive eyes like well-preserved pearls.
As reward for their good deeds.'

55 A New Order

Muhammad had decided to risk everything to undermine the hierarchy of power.

The ruling authority in Mecca felt this threat.

With his texts, Muhammad established a new order of power:

- Allah
- His Prophet
- Believers
- Christians
- Jews
- Nonbelievers

Every day he announced new, groundbreaking laws for the Meccans to live by:

> Women shall inherit half of what men inherit. (This ruling shocked the men. Women, who had never inherited anything before, suddenly had rights to their property.)
>
> Men, women, the wealthy merchants, the male and female slaves; they are all equal before Allah. Those who have done good deeds shall be brought closer to Allah.
>
> Everyone cedes a fifth of his income as gifts, the gifts of Allah.

If a slave asks for his or her freedom, then release them; you may deduct the costs of this freedom from your gifts to Allah.

Help the people who work for you to marry each other, including your virtuous male and female slaves.

Do not abandon your wife once she grows old.

You may only touch your own wives and the female slaves at your disposal; other women are forbidden to you.

There was intense fighting in the streets of Mecca. The city's leaders could no longer sleep peacefully. Things could not go on like this; something had to be done. The agitation Muhammad was causing had to stop.

Then what should have never happened, happened. The Council of Mecca came to a definitive decision. It had to come to an end; it was now or never. They decided to banish Muhammad and his followers from Mecca. To the astonishment of all the residents of the city, a new law was written on a large camel-skin parchment and hung on the wall of the Kaaba for all to see:

'In the name of al-'Uzza, the most important God of the Kaaba, the Council of Mecca decrees:

- It is forbidden to do business with Muhammad and his followers.
- It is forbidden to offer them shelter.
- It is forbidden to give or sell them food.

- It is forbidden to give them a woman or take a woman from them.
- Muhammad and his followers have one day to leave the city.
- Anyone who does not comply with these decrees will be considered a follower of Muhammad.'

It was Friday, the middle of the day, and people stared with amazement at the parchment. Even the oldest men of Mecca could not remember anyone ever being exiled from the city in this way.

56 Aunt Safiyya

Muhammad's advice to his followers was immediately clear, 'Fear not. Nobody needs to leave the city. For the time being, stay at home.'

His followers stayed at home, though this was not so simple. During the first month, there was nothing to complain about but once their bread, meat, and beans ran out, they could no longer evade the questions of their children, wives, and parents.

Nobody dared to sell them anything or have contact with them.

In these difficult times, under cover of dark, Muhammad visited his followers—especially those with a family. He brought treats for their children. He always enjoyed these visits.

I, Zayd, have such fine memories of that time.

One night we visited the black slave Zubayr. He had a son at the time, whose name was Amir. In those days, this Zubayr lived in a barn with his father, mother, wife, and son. Nowadays, he lives in a lovely house in the centre of Mecca.

Unfortunately, Zubayr lost both his legs in one of the many battles he fought for Muhammad in Medina. He is now the grandfather of twenty-three grandchildren and has a fairly good life. He gets around in a sort of cart that was made especially for him.

I went to ask him if he would tell me about the night Muhammad came to visit.

‘Oh, that night,’ said Zubayr, ‘it was such a long time ago, but his unexpected visit still fills me with such warmth. Those days were hard; the nights dismal. My parents were old, Amir was about four years old, and we had nothing left to eat. My wife had been fired from the farm where she worked, and nobody dared to talk to us. I felt powerless.

‘Then, one night, there was an unexpected knock at the door. It was Muhammad, together with you, Zayd, carrying a sack of bread and meat.

‘Muhammad’s presence was like a lantern glowing in the darkness of night.

‘Of course we were grateful that he had brought us bread and meat, but he also did something loving.

‘My son Amir had a bird named Nadir, and he loved that animal. Early that evening, Nadir had suddenly died. Muhammad noticed Amir standing sadly against the wall. I told Muhammad that Amir’s pet bird Nadir had just died. Muhammad knelt before Amir and whispered, “Hey, Amir, what sort of little fellow was Nadir?”

‘The amusing way he spoke to Amir made him burst out in laughter. Later on, every time Muhammad ran into him somewhere, he would call out, “Hey, Amir, what sort of little fellow was Nadir?” Then they would both start laughing.’

Indeed, those were hard days and dark nights. Muhammad, Abu Bakr, Umar, and Uthman individually visited followers every night. They talked with them and prepared them for the difficult period ahead.

Life was testing Muhammad. All eyes were on him. Would he keep up the struggle, or would he break?

Under those difficult circumstances, I watched him grow

from a rebel into a leader. He had control over everything and radiated hope.

One day, his elderly aunt Safiyya came to visit. I took her by the arm and escorted her to Muhammad.

'Aunt Safiyya, what a pleasant surprise. Are you here to sign up as a follower, or have you brought us bread and meat?' he asked with a smile and kissed her hand.

'Muhammad, I've brought you some bread, under one condition,' said Aunt Safiyya with an admonishing finger. 'You must never forget that I'm your aunt; when you were a child I treated you well. I even gave you milk from my own breasts. Will you now do something for me, in return for my bread?'

'Of course, what is it?' said Muhammad, smiling.

'Would you ask your Allah to save me a fine spot in His paradise?'

Muhammad replied seriously, 'I'm sorry, Aunt Safiyya. Elderly women are not allowed into paradise.'

'Then give me back my bread,' said Aunt Safiyya, disappointed, and she grabbed her cane to leave.

'Because elderly women,' Muhammad continued, 'are first turned into fair young maidens again. Only then are they carried to paradise in the arms of handsome young men. I will definitely arrange something for you, Aunt Safiyya.'

57 To the Valley of Abu Talib

Muhammad's followers now faced an all-out famine. For four months, they had managed to put up a strong resistance. Under Uthman's leadership and with Khadija's support a group had been set up that secretly collected food and brought it to Muhammad's followers. But before long the Council of Mecca got wind of the network, and it could not continue its clandestine work.

Muhammad's immediate family continued providing him with grain for his followers, but the family was threatened with a trade ban against their entire clan if they did not break off all contact with Muhammad.

The city council, which feared that Muhammad would actually hold out longer than expected and in this way undermine their decree, decided to expel him and his supporters from the city once and for all.

Umar and Uthman had already gone into hiding, but Abu Bakr—who was the face of the movement—purposely let himself be seen at the market. The city council ordered Abu Bakr's arrest: he had to go into hiding too. Muhammad's house was raided, but he had not lived there for a long time. He had sought refuge in Uncle Talib's house, which no security guard in his right mind would dare to search. And I, Zayd, was Muhammad's only contact with the outside world.

In the meantime, Muhammad had gotten terribly thin. He ate poorly, and his hair was falling out. I saw clumps of it lying everywhere on the floor. He was angry at Allah. He was at odds with Allah.

He did not say it aloud, but he was deeply disappointed in Allah for not helping him through these difficult times, for not giving him a miracle he could show the people. His mission was threatened with failure, and Allah did nothing.

His followers were outlawed, and Allah did nothing.

His men had to go into hiding and were starving, and Allah did nothing.

Allah had helped all the ancient prophets with a miracle when one was needed. Musa threw his cane on the ground and it turned into a snake. Isa cupped a dead bird in his hands, brought it back to life, and let it fly away.

Muhammad wanted something like this as well, something to give his people hope. He wanted to call out to his supporters, 'Hurl your sticks to the ground!' And then all those sticks would change into snakes and go after the Council of Mecca.

Isa asked his God to feed his disciples; to send a table spread with food from heaven. Muhammad also wanted Allah to give his followers bread, but his Allah did not hear him.

I heard Muhammad crying in his hiding place. At moments like these, I waited until he called for me. When I went inside, I saw that his eyes were red, and his beard was drenched in tears.

'These are difficult times, Zayd,' he said, 'but don't despair!'

I stood as still as a statue in the room.

'Have patience, Zayd!' he said.

One night I saw him lying under the blanket with his knees pulled up like a wounded horse. He was groaning. I knew he was receiving a new message from Allah.

'Zayd!' he called short of breath.

I knelt beside him and put my ear to his mouth.

'Go to Abu Bakr's hiding place at once. Tell him I've received a new message. We're leaving the city; we're going to take refuge in his valley.'

58 The Command Given to Yasir

The Valley of Abu Talib was a parched valley, with only a few trees, surrounded by huge rocks.

Each clan had a piece of land where they could spend the hot summers outdoors. There were no dwellings, not even makeshift huts. People slept in the caves or in the openings between the rocks.

Uncle Talib advised Muhammad to go to the valley for the time being and to stay on the land that belonged to their clan until things calmed down in Mecca.

However, this temporary stay lasted three long years. Three terrible years, in which Muhammad desperately tried to keep his followers from losing hope.

Uthman instructed the men to plant vegetables and grain. A sturdy young man named Yasir secretly received a personal task from Umar—he was to steal a goat or camel at night and slaughter it.

It seems like a century has passed since we lived in that valley.

Yesterday I went in search of Yasir. I visited him at his military stronghold outside Mecca on the road to the Red Sea. He had once been the head of supply for the army.

I went on my own horse, which was an animal fit for a prince compared to the horses of ordinary people. Yet, the horses in front of the fortress were even stronger and better trained; elegant animals that greatly impressed the enemy.

'Zayd, you haven't aged a day!' Yasir exclaimed as he received me in his workspace. 'Tell me your secret. How do you do it, what do you eat, and what have you been up to that you stay so young?'

'Muhammad,' I replied, smiling.

Yasir laughed at my answer. We talked seriously about those difficult years in Mecca, and I steered the conversation to the valley, and let him talk:

'Those were important years. You remember, Zayd,' said Yasir, 'we all looked to Muhammad, filled with expectation. If he succumbed, we would all succumb. He did everything to avoid having to kneel at the feet of his enemies. Late at night, he walked in the mountains and talked to himself. We thought he would return with a new mission from Allah, but it wasn't so. We had all grown thin from hunger. We often quarrelled with one another.

'Now that I look back on that period, I see it as an important learning experience. We all came of age in that valley. Umar conquered practically half the world, but without that intense experience in the valley, he would never have managed. Those demanding years in the valley made us tough, made us experienced men who were no longer afraid. We became men of iron there.

'I can sum up my story in one sentence: the Valley of Abu Talib changed the world.'

It was pleasant to talk to Yasir about the past. When I said goodbye and he escorted me to my horse, I jokingly said, 'And you were our number one thief. You stole goats and camels. Without your stolen meat perhaps Muhammad would never have conquered the Kaaba.'

'So you knew?' Yasir reacted, amused. 'I thought it was a secret between Umar and me that I would take to my grave.'

'But where did you get those goats and camels? And how was it possible that nobody figured out the thief was one of Muhammad's followers?'

'Zayd, the children in the valley were hungry. Something had to be done about this. Otherwise how would they have kept up their strength; they would have been forced to leave. One night when I was out walking with Umar, he abruptly stopped on a deserted spot and said, "Yasir, I need meat for the women and children. I don't know how you will do it, but leave at once and don't come back unless you have meat with you. This is a command from above. And it's a secret, which you must bury deep in your heart. Don't ask any questions, don't explain anything. Go! And come back with meat!"'

'Where did you go that night to find a goat? And how is it that you returned early in the morning with a slaughtered camel?'

'Zayd, if you know nothing more, then I have nothing more to tell you,' said Yasir, as he helped me mount my saddle.

59 To Speak or to Remain Silent?

Umar had said to Yasir, 'Don't ask questions; don't explain anything.'

Then what was I allowed to reveal now, and what had to remain a secret? This thought was always in the back of my mind.

Three years of misery had been long enough for us. Muhammad needed to take matters into his own hands, given Allah had not been in touch with him for a while.

'Fetch Abu Bakr, Umar, and Uthman,' Muhammad said to me.

I went to find them right away. It was to be the last meeting in the valley.

They were sitting in a circle in the small cave where they always met to consider their options. I lit a candle and placed it in the middle on the ground. Their shadows fell on the cave walls.

Muhammad looked at Umar and said, 'Today, tonight. And tomorrow it's over.'

Umar replied, 'Tonight, and tomorrow it's over.'

Umar stood up and gestured in my direction, 'You're going with me!'

I did not know where I was going, or what they had planned. I followed Umar, and we descended down into the bottom of the valley, where a black horse was ready and waiting. Umar jumped on and urged me to jump on behind him. With record speed, we rode toward Mecca.

That night remained a secret between Umar and me. Meanwhile, Umar has been murdered. Now I am the only one alive who knows what happened that night. May I tell the story or not? That is the question. It is confidential; information only I know about.

I have thought about this over and over again, and I have reached the following conclusion: if Muhammad did everything to open people's eyes to Allah, then I, Zayd, must do the same for Muhammad.

Meanwhile, I have decided my book may only be read after my death. Umar was able to force the entire Persian Empire to be silent, but he can no longer force me.

Zayd speaks.

60 The Rooftop of the World

I clung to Umar as we galloped through the night toward Mecca. I had no idea what he was planning. The city's main gate was closed and guarded, but Umar had arranged everything. He tied his horse to a tree, pulled a black scarf over his head, and then we cautiously crept along the wall to a small door. He knocked softly, and a watchman immediately opened it. He was one of Muhammad's secret followers who worked as a spy for us. Umar went inside, and I followed. Constantly on our guard, we walked through the dark alleyways to the city centre. There was nobody on the street. Now and then we heard a night watchman and sometimes a guard on horseback passed by.

I realized Umar was heading in the direction of the Kaaba. I wondered what he was going to do there, but I did not ask any questions. I knew that I needed to follow him, in silence.

Large torches illuminated the front side of the Kaaba in the evening, but at night only a small torch burned. There were two guards talking to each other in the dim light.

We walked around the Kaaba to reach the back of the building where it was dark and unguarded as always. It was overwhelming to be there under the cover of night. I touched the wall and got a chill. I needed a moment to pull myself loose from the hold of the idols whose presence I strongly felt.

Umar took out a knife, gave it to me, and whispered, 'Stand on my shoulders and climb onto the roof. Then crawl to the parchment hanging on the wall. Cut the cord, carefully roll up the parchment, and bring it to me.'

I climbed up on Umar's strong shoulders and stepped onto the Kaaba's wooden roof. With the sharp knife between my teeth, I crawled toward the parchment. What an adventure! It felt as if I was crawling across the rooftop of the world. I grabbed one of the two cords, set my knife against it, and cut. Away with this decree that has kept us imprisoned in the valley for three long years. I held the cord securely in my hand and crawled to the other cord. Once I had cut that one too, I tried to roll up the parchment, but it had dried out during those three years hanging in the bright sunlight. It was impossible to roll up and began to fall apart in my hands. So, with some effort, I folded it up, crawled back across the roof, and handed it all to Umar.

I would never forget this experience. When I cut those cords, it felt like I was cutting the reins of power in Mecca. And when I gave the pile of folded parchment to Umar, I knew that a new era had dawned, and nobody could stop it.

I placed my feet back on Umar's shoulders and climbed down from the roof. Then we quickly went on our way.

61 A Joyful Message

Before sunrise, we arrived back in the valley where Muhammad was waiting for us.

'It's done,' Umar exclaimed.

'Fetch Bilal!' Muhammad said to me.

I found Bilal tending the garden he had planted between the rocks with his own hands, to grow potatoes and beets.

'Come with me. Muhammad wants to see you,' I called to him.

He came with me, and Muhammad spoke to him in private.

The sun had just risen, when Bilal went and stood on a hill and announced, 'Listen everyone, I have good news. The time has come. We're going back to Mecca. The decree that exiled us has been destroyed. Allah commanded the ants to eat the parchment. We're going home!'

The news spread through Mecca like wildfire, 'The parchment is gone.'

'Stolen?'

'The ants … the termites devoured it.'

Everybody rushed to the Kaaba to see if the rumour was true. And indeed it was true: the decree was no longer hanging on the wall.

'What will happen now? Will Muhammad return to Mecca?'

'Knowing Muhammad, he will come immediately.'

'Of course. Three years in exile is long enough.'

Rumours quickly spread through the city that Muhammad had left the valley with his followers and would reach Mecca at any moment. A crowd gathered at the city gate.

The sun was high in the sky above Mecca when Muhammad's starving followers and their wives and children with their gaunt faces, torn clothing, long hair, and bare feet entered the city. A straight-backed Muhammad was at the head of the group. His beard had turned completely grey. He did not make eye contact with anyone. His face was expressionless, as if he was wearing an iron mask, so nobody could read his emotions and thoughts.

The people of Mecca stared at him in silence. Nobody applauded, nobody jeered. It was completely quiet. Only the footsteps of Muhammad and his followers could be heard. And the city's security guards stayed calm and kept their distance.

Muhammad had instructed all of his followers to go back to their homes and family and to rest.

The Valley of Abu Talib was now part of history. Muhammad already had other things on his mind. Soon a new sura would be revealed to him.

62 Saluma, the Servant of Khadija

A few months passed, and not much of anything happened. It was quiet on the streets, and the followers went to the market like ordinary Meccans, without saying anything about Muhammad or his Qur'an.

It seemed like Muhammad had learned his lesson and had decided to stay in the background. Everyone saw it as a time for reflection. Nobody could predict that Muhammad would once again stir things up, just like before.

Muhammad had indeed instructed his followers to lay low and take the time they needed to recover. In reality, there was something else going on. The severity of life in the valley had taken its toll.

Three years earlier, when Muhammad had been forced to leave the city, his elderly uncle Talib went with him as a form of protest against the city council's decision. And he stayed in the valley until the very last day to support Muhammad. With his mere presence, he protected Muhammad.

After returning to Mecca, Uncle Talib fell ill, and a month later he died.

Muhammad had not yet recovered from this blow, when his wife Khadija also died. Her health had been seriously compromised in the valley. Khadija had lived her entire life in luxury, without knowing harsh times. She was not made to live outdoors among the rocks like a peasant. Even so, she had managed for three years, but once she was back in her own bed, she never left it again.

Now, decades after her death, I needed to find the right person to tell me about Khadija's final days. I thought of Saluma, Khadija's handmaiden.

When she went to the valley with Khadija, Saluma was a beautiful young woman.

She was the colour of ebony, had brown eyes, perky breasts, shapely full lips, and an enticing sway in her hips.

When I saw Saluma again, she had completely changed. Now she was a woman of around fifty.

Her breasts were cumbersome, her swaying bottom had sagged, and she had lost the sparkle in her eyes. She had given birth to ten children, who in turn gave her seventeen grandchildren. Yet, she still had something of her former allure. Her hips made the same delightful swaying movement I remembered from the past.

'Zayd! Is it you? It can't be true. Yes, it's you. How is it possible?'

'I wanted to admire your graceful movements once more.'

'Then, go on, come inside and admire them!'

Saluma was still well versed in the art of seduction. I complimented her, but she playfully laughed it off.

'You're not here for me, Zayd. Tell me, how can I help you?'

'Of course, I'm curious how you're doing, Saluma. But you're right, I'm here about *Khadrat* Khadija. Actually, I want to talk to you about the last days you spent with the honourable Khadija. Would you mind telling me about that time?'

'Zayd, you want to take me back to those beautiful but painful days in that house. Listen, my mistress Khadija was already quite ill in the valley, but she kept this to herself. She did not want to make things more difficult for Muhammad. When she returned home to Mecca, she went straight to bed. She had grown so weak she could not walk anymore.

'Muhammad knew she was dying because their physician had told him. He was heartbroken and rarely left Khadija's side. He knelt beside her bed and stroked her head. She was old and had gotten frail and thin in the mountains. Muhammad's body was still strong, and he emanated power. He lay down next to her and put his head beside hers. On the last day, Khadija came down with a high fever. I fetched some water, and Muhammad washed her feet and dabbed her forehead with wet cloths. In the early morning, when I heard Muhammad sobbing, I knew Khadija was gone.'

63 Musab, the Great Qur'anic Scholar

Muhammad became very withdrawn after Uncle Talib's death, but after Khadija died, he was more withdrawn than ever. He went into seclusion, and his self-imposed exile lasted so long, it confused the members of the Council of Mecca. They wondered if Muhammad was intentionally keeping a low profile now that he was back, or if his silence indicated he was making sinister plans. Something was going on, but what was it?

To describe that period, I needed to talk to somebody who had experienced it first-hand, and nobody was more qualified than Musab bin Jalil Abbas, the great Qur'anic scholar of our time.

He was one of the first followers to intensively study Muhammad's texts. Muhammad had difficulty reciting his own words; he did not completely trust his memory and quickly rambled off sentences one after another. That is also the reason he stuttered. But Musab had an impeccable memory, recited the texts with confidence, jotted them down, and explained them in a way that surprised even Muhammad.

In search of Musab, I went to Mecca's new mosque, where he taught the Qur'an.

Musab not only had an impeccable memory, he was a captivating speaker as well.

'We lived in the valley and there I taught the followers to read and write,' he said. Muhammad's tales united his followers during those difficult days in the mountains. When they could finally read Muhammad's words by themselves, they felt complete.

‘One night, Muhammad wanted to speak to me alone, so we went and sat on the top of the mountain together.

‘Muhammad said, “Allah has commanded me to spread Islam in the city of Yathrib. You, Musab, have a way with words. This is an exceptional mission, and Allah has chosen you for it. We’ve made the first contacts in the city. You’ll take some of our strongest men and settle in Yathrib. I’ll make sure you have lodgings there. You must build a network in Yathrib: a network of new followers. Is this clear?”

“Muhammad is the messenger,” I said, “and it’s perfectly clear what the messenger wants of me.”

‘The next day I packed up Muhammad’s texts and set off on foot toward Yathrib, with six other followers.’

I, Zayd, can still clearly remember that day. It was early morning. Muhammad embraced his followers, kissed them, and chanted a short sura in their left ear. That is how they were sent off. Nobody knew where they were going. I did not know either. The agreement was between Muhammad and Musab.

But why were they going to Yathrib?

‘Two ancient Arab clans lived in Yathrib, alongside the Jews and a small Christian community,’ said Musab. ‘The power was in the hands of the Jews, and the comings and goings on the market were determined by them. They were wealthy and lent money with steep interest rates. Actually, in one way or another, almost everybody had debts by a Jew.

‘These two Arab clans were always fighting, and the Jews sometimes supported one clan and then the other, also to play them against each other. For centuries, they had looked down on the Arabs, for they, the Jews, had a Holy Book but the Arabs did not.

‘Muhammad knew the Arabs hated the powerful Jews. His maternal uncles and aunts all lived in Yathrib, and he knew the city inside out. The Jews were also Muhammad’s staunchest enemies in Mecca. They belittled him, humiliated him, and had contempt for his texts. They openly accused him of plagiarizing their Torah.

“Muhammad? A prophet? Please, he’s an illiterate thief,” said the Jews.

‘I think Muhammad had already reached the following conclusions in the valley: “It’s not feasible to accomplish anything more in Mecca; I must take my followers to Yathrib. I shall reconcile the city’s two Arab tribes, comfort them with the Qur’an, make the Jews subservient, and seize power over the city.”’

This was the story Musab told me.

64 The Heavenly City of Yathrib

Let me tell you something more about Yathrib. The city is quite far from Mecca; by camel, it takes about three weeks travelling. Mecca has a dry climate; in comparison, Yathrib is a paradise. The vast green fields are covered in beautiful, tall date palms under which rivers flow. The camels feed on fresh grass instead of the dry thorns of Mecca. Swarms of buzzing bees fly from one field of wild flowers to another, the wind is gentle and smells of the sea, and birds soar serenely through the blue sky.

Moreover, the women of Mecca are solidly built, with large hands and feet. The warm wind and the sand have parched their skin dry, but Yathrib's women, with their delicate bodies and rosy skin, are beautiful. You can drown in their eyes.

Muhammad drew his inspiration for the heavenly gardens in the Qur'an from the poetic scenery of Yathrib:

> 'Muhammad! Recount the good news to those who believe you when you say that there are gardens set aside for them, under which rivers flow. That there will be pretty male and female companions for them, and they have a dwelling there for eternity.'

Muhammad felt connected to Yathrib. His mother Amina was born there, his father was buried there, and a large part of his family still lived there.

After being exiled to the valley, Muhammad sent Musab, his most learned follower, to Yathrib to plant a seed that would produce new followers. And the soil of Yathrib seemed ready to receive the words of Muhammad. It was not an action that would reap benefits right away; Muhammad would have to be patient for a few years. He was used to being patient.

Everything that happened took place in utter secrecy. The Council of Mecca kept a close watch on everything they could, but it did not occur to them that Muhammad was also active in Yathrib.

They knew he had not abandoned his mission, but assumed he would keep a low profile after the severe punishment he had suffered. In fact, Muhammad was the one who preserved the peace in Mecca. The violent demonstrations were something of the past. The followers regularly gathered at quiet places, and when Muhammad invited people to follow him, his tone was much softer than before.

New people did join the movement, but the amount was not large enough to worry the Council of Mecca.

There seemed to be a silent agreement between Muhammad and the city council. The authorities tolerated him. After all, in a few years he would be old, and all his strange assertions would simply stop.

Clearly, they had not learned anything about Muhammad. It had not occurred to the city council that Muhammad had already reached his own conclusions, 'Mecca is beyond our reach. We can't possibly conquer the city from within. So we shall go to Yathrib. We will raise our swords there, and then we'll return to conquer Mecca.'

He had a plan for Yathrib. He wanted to make the city the heart of the empire he dreamed of creating.

All the suras revealed to him in this period included a recurring sentence, 'Muhammad, be patient!'

Mecca got quieter by the day. People did not realize that Muhammad was secretly sending his followers to Yathrib one after another. After two years, his efforts in Yathrib began to bear fruit. There was more and more talk on the street about the messenger Muhammad, about the Qur'an, and about Allah who is One. Yathrib's shopkeepers increasingly cited the Qur'an when they found themselves in discussion with the Jews.

The Qur'an did not exist as a book yet, but the quotes that were carved on wood and in camel bones were displayed in public. The new followers in Yathrib made the long journey to Mecca to meet with Muhammad in secret.

Disguised as a simple trader, Abu Bakr travelled to Yathrib. He approached the chieftains of the Arab tribes and officially talked to them about uniting against the powerful Jews who had the city in their grip. 'We are offering you an Arabic Book and a leader.'

65 Abbas, the Mediator of Muhammad

Muhammad had a third uncle, whose name was Abbas. He was a wealthy merchant in Mecca and had good contacts with Yathrib's prominent merchants. He was not one of Muhammad's supporters but not one of his adversaries either. Abbas was a pleasure seeker, a loner who steered clear of the politics in Mecca. However, he always maintained a good relationship with Muhammad.

I, Zayd, visited Abbas one night, carrying a personal message from Muhammad.

Abbas' home was large and impressive. I had never seen a house quite like this one. There were finely crafted cabinets all around the elegant living room, and large chandeliers hanging from the ceiling.

Abbas poured wine into his cup and said, 'So tell me, Zayd, why are you here?'

I whispered, 'Muhammad the messenger wants to see you. He'd like to set up a secret meeting.'

Abbas was a lovely fellow. He was slightly drunk and laughed aloud, 'I like this Muhammad of yours. Tell him we'll arrange it. He raised his cup and exclaimed, 'Long live the messenger!'

Two nights later, by way of the garden door, I entered Abbas' house together with Muhammad. Abbas welcomed Muhammad with open arms, 'Muhammad, what can I do for you?'

'Put me in touch with Yathrib's clan chieftains,' Muhammad said straightforwardly.

Abbas was a clever man and immediately guessed what Muhammad was up to. They sat down on a couch and deliberated the rest of the night. I stood guard at the door.

A week later, Abbas travelled to Yathrib with a caravan of goods. Through the mediation of his friends, he was allowed to visit the Arab chieftains. It was the first of many meetings; Abbas would have to travel to Yathrib a number of times before he could bring Muhammad in contact with the clan chieftains. More than a year passed before the time was right.

Two of the most important chieftains travelled to Mecca, and Abbas received them in his grand house without anybody getting wind of this. During a dinner fit for a king, he introduced Muhammad to them.

The leader of the Aus tribe was called Abu Yajzan bin Yasib bin Amir bin Malik bin Kinaja bin Ghiz bin Husayn bin Luzayn. That is: Abu Yajzan, the son of Yasib, the son of Amir, the son of Malik, the son of Kinaja, the son of Ghiz, the son of Husayn, the son of Luzayn. This Abu Yajzan lived to be ninety-two years old, had fifty-three children from nine wives and thirteen slaves, and a countless number of grandchildren and descendants.

The leader of the Khazraj tribe was called Abu Huzighi bin Mughiri bin Abdullah bin Uzar bin Makhzum. He lived to be seventy-six years old and had thirteen sons and twenty-seven daughters.

Muhammad talked with them deep into the night while Abbas plied them with delicacies and drinks. Together they reached a decision.

Muhammad wanted to leave Mecca, and the chieftains would receive and protect him.

In this way, Muhammad took the first essential step on his way to achieving power. He would stay in Mecca until his last followers had secretly left the city. Then he would leave as well.

With the support and approval of these two chieftains, Muhammad became a well-known figure in Yathrib.

Many young people became followers, and they in turn offered shelter to Muhammad's followers arriving from Mecca.

Things were gradually set in motion in the city of Yathrib, and the followers held gatherings on the market square. The arrival of our orator Bilal, with his mysterious voice, caused a stir in the city. He stood at the busy crossroads with Muhammad's followers and recited texts of the Qur'an to passers-by.

From Yathrib, Umar sent Muhammad a note. I read it aloud to him, 'The city is aglow with happiness. Everybody awaits Muhammad's arrival.'

66 The Flight

Of course, by now, the stories about Muhammad's new followers had reached Mecca. But Yathrib was far away. What happened there could not possibly disturb the peace and order in Mecca. Yet, Mecca was buzzing when the news of the secret meeting between Muhammad and the chieftains of Yathrib leaked out.

Only then did people realize that Muhammad's followers had slowly been leaving Mecca, 'Hey, the nests are empty, the birds have flown the coop.'

At the marketplace, everybody was talking about the secret meeting:

'Oh, that sly fox Muhammad.'

'Clever fellow!'

'How did he manage to bring Yathrib's two hostile tribes together?'

'Are all his followers gone?'

'Where did they go? When did they leave?'

'Muhammad has also left.'

'No, that's not true. This morning, I saw him strolling on the Kaaba Square with Abu Bakr.'

It was true; Muhammad was still around. He was waiting until all his followers had left Mecca, and every morning and afternoon, he intentionally took a walk on the market to mislead the Council of Mecca. However, this diversion did not work anymore because the Council had made a decision. No matter the cost, they wanted Muhammad dead before he had a chance to flee. They knew that once he reached Yathrib, he would become great and powerful. Then nobody could stop him.

However, Muhammad was no longer the old Muhammad, the gentle-hearted man. He had become a cunning leader. He had accomplices everywhere, also on the Council of Mecca. Therefore, he was immediately informed that they were planning to murder him in his bed that evening.

Umar and Uthman were in Yathrib. Only Abu Bakr was in Mecca with Muhammad.

Muhammad devised a ruse.

'Fetch Ali,' he instructed me.

Ali had grown into a strong young man and was about the same height and build as Muhammad. In the dark, one could not distinguish the two from each other. And Ali was brave. Muhammad told him the plan.

Ali put on Muhammad's coat, lit the lantern, opened the curtains halfway, and stood behind the window so his shadow fell across the curtain. Anybody outside, looking through the window, would think Muhammad was in his room. And I, Zayd, stayed by Ali's side.

Muhammad and Abu Bakr disappeared over the rooftops into the darkness. Moments after they left, seven men appeared in the alleyway by Muhammad's house. They scaled the walls to the roof, came down the stairs, and quietly crept toward Muhammad's room where Ali and I were waiting for them. I had left the door ajar and was hiding behind it, in the darkness. Ali had taken up position between the lantern and the curtain. I saw the men entering the room, their daggers raised in their hands. But before they made their way inside, I shouted at the top of my lungs, 'Don't move!'

67 The Spider

I was not at Muhammad's side when he fled, and I had no idea where he went that night. Later, Muhammad told me exactly what happened himself. And I transcribed his words in the sura 'Contrition':

> 'If you do not want to help His prophet, Allah shall help him as He did before, when some wanted to kill him, and he fled to the mountains with Abu Bakr, a companion. They sought refuge in a cave. He said to his companion, "Do not be discouraged. Allah is with us!" God sent down his rest upon them. A spider appeared and closed the entrance to the cave so that the men who were pursuing them were unable to see them. Allah can do all things!'

It became a story that everyone passed from one person to the next; it got more elaborate over the years. People added many things and also removed many things, but I shall tell it how it really was:

Muhammad and Abu Bakr fled into the mountains, pursued by the same seven men who had been sent to murder Muhammad. The assassins saw two silhouettes moving on the mountainside. By way of different mountain passes, they ascended the slope and surrounded the fleeing men. Muhammad and Abu Bakr were trapped. Suddenly, they noticed the entrance to a small cave. They crawled inside. Then, all at once, a large spider appeared and started to weave a dense web in front of the cave opening.

When the assassins arrived, they could not find Muhammad and Abu Bakr anywhere. They knew they had to be hiding in the vicinity. Of course they did see the cave, but it was closed off by the spider web. They continued on and spent two nights and three more days searching the mountainside. Muhammad and Abu Bakr were like two drops of rain that had evaporated in the parched mountains.

Of course, I, Zayd, do not know exactly what happened during Muhammad's flight through the mountains. And I don't know what Muhammad and Abu Bakr agreed to in the cave. Based on my own observations, though, I think their conversation must have gone something like this:

Muhammad said, 'Now that we've burned all our bridges, there's no way back. We must take up the sword and fight to the death to conquer Mecca.

Abu Bakr replied, 'Until now we were comrades; from today on we are united for all eternity. And to consecrate this sworn bond between us, I give you my daughter Aisha.'

I believe Aisha, the daughter of Abu Bakr, was around nine years old at the time, and Muhammad was over fifty. Thus, Muhammad became Abu Bakr's son-in-law, and Abu Bakr became Muhammad's father-in-law.

Afterwards, they continued their flight to safety on foot, following the Red Sea to Yathrib. During the journey, to cover more ground, they purchased two camels from a farmer.

68 A New Era

Muhammad had fled. And I, Zayd, was supposed to go with Ali to Yathrib that same night. But I stayed behind. Unfortunately, this caused me to miss a part of Muhammad's life that was very important historically.

It could not be helped.

Later, when we were putting together a new calendar, we designated Muhammad's flight from Mecca to Yathrib as the beginning of the Islamic Era. On that day, the world of Islam began.

I shall let Musab, the great Qur'anic Scholar, continue with his story. He is probably the best person to recount that part of Muhammad's life. After all, he was the one who Muhammad had sent to Yathrib a few years earlier to offer the Qur'an to the people and create new groups of followers.

When Muhammad was on the run, Musab lived in Yathrib and was aware of everything going on there.

According to him, Muhammad's escape had caused an uproar in Yathrib. It was the talk of the town; everybody was tense—waiting for news:

'Perhaps they've arrested him?'

'He's clever. He's not going to fall into their clutches.'

'He's the messenger. His Allah will help him.'

'But if he's still alive, why haven't we heard anything from him?'

'He'll come. Any day now, he will appear out of the blue.'

'I finally got some good news,' Musab said. 'Muhammad was alive and well, and he and Abu Bakr had reached the village of Quba by travelling the coast. They would be in Yathrib within a few days. I made the news public. The followers climbed up on the roofs and shouted, "Glad tidings! The messenger is on his way!"

'Nobody had expected this. People from all the Arab clans flooded the streets, cheering. They beat on drums and handed out dates and sweets. From one day to the other, the Arabs had received a messenger with a Book that was even more beautiful and more powerful than the Book of the Jews. Because people were not well versed in the Torah or the Gospel of Isa, the texts that our Bilal recited with his melodious voice were so exciting, so mysterious, that no other texts could surpass the beauty of the Qur'an.'

Three days later, as Muhammad approached the city of Yathrib, all the Arabs closed their shops, and crowds of people headed for the city gate—including the women, children, and slaves—to welcome Muhammad.

The Jews stayed home, but the Christians—who had been tormented by the Jews for centuries because of their nondescript Isa—secretly joined forces with the Arabs. This changed the balance of power in the city in one fell swoop.

Thousands of people were waiting at the city gate. Two camels appeared in the distance; the silhouettes of two men were visible. The crowd let out a cry of joy. As the travellers approached, they shouted:

'Muhammad is the messenger!'

'We welcome the messenger!'

The crowd pressed forward to catch a glimpse of him, and people called his name to offer him a place to stay.

Muhammad dropped the camel's reins and said, 'Where my camel kneels, is where I'll dwell.'

The camel slowly walked through the gate and lumbered from one street to another while the crowd followed in silence. It passed many houses. Everyone hoped the camel would kneel in front of their home, but the animal entered a narrow alley, stopped by a low door, knelt, and laid its long neck on the ground. This house was the place where Muhammad's mother had been born and where Muhammad's father had died.

The residents of Yathrib gave the camel the honorary name al-Qaswa, the one who comes from afar. Because the population of Yathrib took such good care of al-Qaswa, the camel lived a very long life. Years later, it died of natural causes.

69 A Wife for Zayd

In the city of Yathrib, everything changed for Muhammad.

Yathrib was given a new name: Madinat al-Nabi which meant 'The City of the Prophet'.

Medina for short.

Muhammad started a new life in Medina.

Khadija had died, Mecca was far away, and in Medina, he was not only treated as a real prophet but also considered the leader of the Arab tribes. The gates of an earthly paradise opened for Muhammad. He did not need Abu Bakr's nine-year-old daughter as his wife, because the young, kind-hearted women of Medina gladly offered themselves to him, 'Messenger, take me! Bless me!'

And Muhammad blessed them.

He had always been faithful to Khadija, but now he was completely taken with all the young women who threw themselves at him. He went so far that even Allah reprimanded him, 'That's enough Muhammad!' He listened, was content with his lawful wives and the countless beautiful slave girls he later received as spoils of war.

I, Zayd, want to tell you something very personal, but I hesitate to do so.

I had best put down my pen for a moment, to give this some more thought …

Okay, shall I tell you the story?

It went like this:

Muhammad was the messenger.

Abu Bakr became the first Caliph.

Umar became the second Caliph.

Uthman became the third Caliph.

Ali became the fourth Caliph.

And Zayd became the chronicler.

I give you my word that this is the truth: we were still living in Mecca, and, according to the words of Abu Bakr, I had become a strong man, an extraordinary man. Muhammad had a beautiful cousin. So stunning, she reminded you of a crescent moon in the night sky. Her name was Zaynab. She was around seventeen.

One night, Muhammad called me, 'Zayd! I need to speak to you.'

We strolled along the river under the date palms and talked. He said, 'Zayd, you're a man now. What do you think of Zaynab?'

I was startled by his unexpected question. I did not respond. I did not know what to say. I had never thought about Zaynab, I did not dare. She was so lovely, so graceful; she could never be mine.

The next day, Muhammad placed Zaynab's hand in mine, recited a sura and blessed our marital union. That is how Zaynab became my wife. Zaynab slept beside me and grew more and more beautiful as the days passed. She was like a ray of sunshine in my house, and every night I lay my head on the pillow next to hers.

However, once we moved to Medina, Zaynab was no longer

interested in me but in Muhammad. She wanted to be admired by the messenger, not by his servant. One day, she was standing naked washing herself in a large copper tub in the middle of our courtyard. At that moment, Muhammad appeared unexpectedly. His gaze fell upon Zaynab in all her beauty.

I was inside by the window and saw Muhammad's reaction. He closed his eyes and said, '*Fa-tabaraka llahu 'ahsanu l-khaliqin*. So blessed is Allah, the best of Creators. Allah, who has created so much beauty.'

Zaynab overheard him reciting this, and from that moment on she no longer slept beside me. She knew Muhammad desired her. And then Zaynab left my house. I had no choice but to distance myself from her, to let her go.

Muhammad was angry with me.

I remained silent.

Muhammad ordered me to fetch my wife and bring her home.

I remained silent.

Allah sent a sura to curse me.

I remained silent.

Muhammad slept beside my Zaynab for several nights. Then he announced a new rule:

'Oh, you who believe! Do not enter the houses of others without asking or without greeting those who dwell there with "Salaam!" First you must knock on the door. Warn the inhabitants. And when you enter, you must always exclaim, "Salaam" so all can hear, a salaam to the house and a salaam to those who dwell here.'

Zaynab became Muhammad's seventh wife.

70 Mecca and Medina

The Muhammad of Medina bore no resemblance to the Muhammad of Mecca.

In Mecca, he was insulted, beaten, and they wanted to kill him. In Mecca, his prose was gentle, and his texts lent themselves to poetry. In Mecca, he was not interested in women, he ate poorly, and hardly laughed. He was gaunt, always agonizing, and his hair was falling out.

In Mecca, he was a rebel. In Mecca, he was a family man and Khadija's husband. In Mecca, his strategy was about defending himself.

But in Medina, he became the leader of the city. In Medina, he took pleasure in women, ate like an Arabian horse, enjoying grapes, figs, and olives. He stuck his whole finger into the honey jar and licked it clean. He did not wait for his nine-year-old wife Aisha to mature. He rubbed olive oil through his hair and made love to Aisha.

In Medina, his prose became violent—defensive tactics were clearly no longer needed. In Medina, his posture was more upright, and he became a shrewd politician. He negotiated, made use of political lies, and came up with dirty tricks.

In Medina, he laid the foundation for his Islamic reign. He compiled a code of law with fifty-two rules based on all sorts of beliefs, to help the inhabitants of the city to get along with one another. In this way, he presented himself as the leader of the entire population, including the Jews and Christians. To quell the persistent protests of the Jews, he came up with a strategy and reached a compromise with them, worth its weight in gold, 'You may practice your own faith, but when it comes to war, you will stand with me and fight against my enemies.

'And in return, I and my followers will do two things; we shall pray facing the direction of your Holy Sanctuary in Jerusalem, and we shall fast with you.'

The Jews took this as a sign that Muhammad still respected the ancient Jewish faith, so they reluctantly agreed.

Then Muhammad invited the Christian leaders to his new mosque, which was still being built, and told them the following:

'I love your prophet Isa. Maryam could also be my mother. But I don't appreciate your lies; that Isa is the son of Allah. My stomach turns every time I see a priest making the sign of the cross, "The Father, the Son, and the Holy Spirit. Amen."

'It's an open attack against Allah. Allah is One! He was not fathered, nor does He father. Allah has no son.'

An agreement was reached with the city's most influential priests: Christians would no longer make the sign of the cross in public nor openly refer to Isa as the Son of God.

In exchange, Muhammad would protect the city's Christians against the continuing humiliation and violence at the hands of the Jews.

Muhammad now had the necessary elements to solidify his reign of power:

He had compiled a Code of Law with fifty-two rules.

He had built a gathering place for his followers: the mosque.

He had designated a sacred place to which his followers

could direct their prayers: Jerusalem.

He had equipped a number of forges, where blacksmiths worked day and night making swords for him. And he had set up a camp where his followers were being trained for battle.

He accomplished all of this in the first year of his stay in Medina.

The only thing he still lacked was money or gold.

71 In the Mosque

In Medina, Muhammad was almost never at home. He did not even have a bedroom of his own nor a wife. In fact, Muhammad lived in his mosque. He was in love with his mosque. One could find him there at any moment, day or night. The mosque became the heart of his religious movement; the place where all decisions were made. Decisions taken outside of the mosque were not valid.

The mosque was built on the edge of the city centre. In the beginning, the windows opened toward Jerusalem and overlooked a beautiful landscape covered in lush gardens with grapevines, almond trees, and olive trees. These were the Gardens of Bliss in Paradise, as Muhammad had described them. A large window at the rear of the mosque offered a view of the mountains.

Muhammad proudly wandered the grounds of his mosque and talked freely with his followers, who tended to the gardens.

I had seldom seen him so cheerful in Mecca; now his laugh resounded throughout the mosque.

The constant attention he also received from the women of Medina made him look younger and more handsome. In Mecca, at times, he suffered from the insults and stress. In Medina, he sat tall in his saddle, rode his horse onto the market square like a king, and beamed with happiness when the women pointed, 'Look. There he is! The messenger.'

Abu Nuwas, the court poet of Medina, once wrote a poem about Muhammad's horse:

'Is there truly a woman to be found
whose braids are softer than
the mane of Muhammad horse?
Is there truly a woman to be found
whose breasts are more shapely
than the saddle of Muhammad's horse?
Where can a woman be found
whose eyes shine as brightly
as the eyes of Muhammad's horse?
No, there isn't a single woman
who quivers with excitement,
like Muhammad's horse
on the battlefield,
and still remains calm.'

Like Muhammad, I carried a sword and rode a clever, black horse. I learned to fight in the military camp where the followers were being trained.

Medina was the happiest city in the world—because it had seventy sorts of dates, with seventy different names—and would become the centre of a great new civilization.

72 Salman Farsi, the Persian Warlord

Muhammad and his advisers went and sat in a circle on the floor in the middle of the mosque's prayer space. I quietly walked along the windows, keeping a close eye on everything happening inside as well as outside.

The nature of these meetings in the mosque was different from those held in the past at Muhammad's house in Mecca. There was more talk about combat tactics and gold, weapons, and food. Umar had made contact with a few former Persian warlords, and three of them were prepared to come to Medina to advise Muhammad.

One of them was called Salman, better known as Salman Farsi. He would later become Muhammad's personal war adviser. He was in his thirties by then, a clever man and an ingenious inventor of new combat methods. Salman supervised the training camps and the workshops where weapons were made.

It was one of the last nights of the first year following Muhammad's escape to Medina. Salman and Muhammad were alone in the mosque. They had unrolled a map and were bending over it, deep in discussion.

When their conversation ended, Muhammad called me over.

I placed my hand on my sword and rushed to him.

He rattled off the names of forty men, and I quickly jotted these down. 'Before sunrise. On Mount Uhud. With their swords in hand. And they're not to be told about one another.'

I jumped on my horse and rode with breakneck speed through the city to alert the men.

Before dawn the next day, all the men gathered at the foot of Mount Uhud. It was still dark so it was difficult for them to make out one another's faces. They were instructed not to talk and had no idea what lay ahead. Muhammad arrived and said, 'Last night I received a new message from Allah. Soon, an important trade caravan with gold and goods, travelling from Mecca via the Red Sea route, will enter the valley.

'We're going to attack the caravan and seize the gold and money for the mosque. A third of the stolen goods will be split between all of you, the rest is for the mosque.'

Nobody moved; everyone listened silently.

'Are there any questions?'

'But Muhammad, it is still the holy month of Ramadan. War is forbidden during Ramadan. Why are we doing this?' one of the followers asked.

'It isn't my decision,' Muhammad replied. 'I don't know why. Allah decides. He is all-knowing. And this is no ordinary war; this is a holy war. A war for Allah.'

'Muhammad, is it just a raid, or is it really a war?' another asked.

'It's a holy raid. That's the message I received.'

There were no more questions. Muhammad instructed everyone to take up position on the mountain.

The caravan entered the valley.

Muhammad loudly cried, *'La 'ilaha 'illa llah!* There is one God: Allah.'

The followers cried, 'Allah' in unison and attacked the

caravan. Caught off guard, in disbelief, the defeated traders abandoned their horses, camels, and goods, and fled into the mountains.

We returned to a jubilant Medina with thirteen hundred and fifty-three horses and camels loaded down with gold and goods.

73 The First Battle with Mecca

After the holy raid, as Muhammad's men paraded for him in front of the mosque wielding their weapons, the poet Abu Nuwas climbed onto a platform and dedicated this poem to them:

'You! My sword!
When I feel your razor-sharp edge
I feel like I'm caressing the tender breasts
Of a young Bedouin woman.
And when I hold you,
I feel like I'm cradling a bunch of sweet, ripe, red grapes
in the palm of my hand.
I am not burdened by hunger or thirst.
And the ripe fruit and pleasures of delightful gardens
Will not deter me when I'm galloping on my horse,
with you in my hand.'

After this first raid, Muhammad's followers acquired a taste for looting, and the ambushes that followed were equally successful. Now everybody wanted to join Muhammad. Each day, from far and near, dozens of young men and adventurers arrived in Medina and found their way to the mosque to sign up with Umar.

The plundering along the caravan routes shocked Mecca. Muhammad's escapades threatened all of Mecca's trade with ruin. Not a single merchant dared to leave the city, and nobody dared to travel to Mecca.

Something had to be done. They had to capture Muhammad and destroy his army before it became too powerful.

Abu Sufyan, the military commander of Mecca, devised a plan. He sent nine hundred and fifty of his fighters, disguised as merchants, with a caravan in the direction of Medina. He arranged for Muhammad to hear about this large transport of gold and goods approaching Medina via the Red Sea route.

Muhammad's men had carried out the first raid barefoot, with their bare hands. Now they had horses, fast camels, and sharp lightweight swords at their disposal. As a result, they needed sufficient space and could not attack the enemy in narrow valley passes anymore.

This time Muhammad chose the desert, and his fighters hid from view behind the sandhills. But when they attacked the caravan, against all expectation, they were confronted by heavily armed fighters from Mecca's army.

Muhammad's men, who had prepared themselves for looting the caravan's gold and valuables, were shocked by this unforeseen turn of events.

What should Muhammad do? He quickly consulted with Salman Farsi and Abu Bakr.

If they returned to Medina now, they would be pursued by Mecca's army and bring the war to the streets of the city. They had to stay and fight, there was no turning back. Salman advised brief, fast offensives, 'Attack, hit hard, and swiftly retreat.'

To encourage his followers, Muhammad shouted, 'Whoever dies here, goes straight to paradise. Whoever lives gets gold!'

We attacked the caravan 137 times, we succeeded in weakening the lengthy caravan's defences 137 times, and we retreated 137 times. Part of the enemy camp was slain, some were taken prisoner, and some managed to escape. Fourteen men died fighting at Muhammad's side.

The first official war between Mecca and Muhammad had unexpectedly taken place, and Muhammad had won. The news spread throughout the realm. Muhammad was no longer a rebel leader. He had achieved the status of a warlord.

To get a good glimpse of the triumphant procession and to count the spoils, I, Zayd, was up in the gate tower overlooking Medina. The inhabitants of the city were lined up in two rows just outside the gateway, cheering for Muhammad.

I listed what we had captured:
723 camels loaded with swords, combat materials, and phony merchandise
93 trained battle horses
73 camels loaded with food and drink
13 camels loaded with pans and cooking utensils
23 camels loaded with clothing and shoes
126 prisoners of war
47 young women who had accompanied the caravan

No money. No gold.

74 War

Eighteen months after Mecca suffered its humiliating defeat, it sent an army of three thousand men led by Abu Sufyan himself to attack Medina. The Jews took part in secret. They supported Mecca's army with manpower as well as horses, camels, food, and weapons.

Muhammad went to meet Abu Sufyan in battle with seven hundred men.

The poet Abu Nuwas wrote a poem for Medina's women to encourage their fighters:

> 'You! Warriors of Muhammad!
> Attack your enemy without mercy.
> Then we will welcome you with the soft silk
> Adorning our bodies,
> And let you taste and enjoy yet another kind of pleasure.
> But if you turn your back on the enemy,
> No more cups of wine will we serve you,
> And all other kinds of pleasures will end.'

Yet, these seductive words of encouragement from Medina's women did not produce the desired results, and Muhammad's warriors were deprived of 'all other kinds of pleasure' for quite some time.

The decisive war began, and Muhammad's men followed him into battle on their trained horses, moving as a single unit. I,

Zayd, always rode on the outside of the unit to keep an eye on the group. The military, war, and the sword were not for me. I was only an eyewitness, the eyewitness to Muhammad's life. Yes, I carried a sword but I never fought with it. Nor did I kill anyone.

I wore a sword for two reasons: to protect Muhammad if somebody tried to attack him from behind, and to defend myself, if necessary.

I think everybody was only thinking about the money and gold they would soon bring back to Medina as spoils of war. However, this did not turn out as expected. We were unable to implement any of our combat tactics. Their attack was so overpowering, we did not know what hit us. In that battle, I tasted the fiery hell Muhammad so often described.

Abu Sufyan, the military commander of Mecca, had chosen a battle tactic from the ancient Romans. We attacked the enemy from the front as well as the rear but to no avail. When we fled to the right, they were waiting for us. When we fled to the left, they were waiting for us. There was no way out, unless Allah gave each of us two strong wings to ascend into the sky.

Many perished, and those who managed to flee threw down their swords, let their horses loose, fled into the desert, and hid behind a sandhill to save their lives.

Muhammad cried, 'Come back! Men, come back!'

Nobody listened to him.

Muhammad cried, 'Men, look up in the sky! Allah is sending angels to fight alongside us.'

Nobody looked up; nobody wanted to see the angels.

Umar, Uthman, Abu Bakr, and Salman rode at full speed

to Medina to take up position at the gate and defend the city against a possible attack.

Abu Sufyan's army jubilantly celebrated its victory. They waved their swords in the air and rode circles on horseback, shouting wildly. And they had it right. Not a single one of Muhammad's fighters was anywhere to be found on the front line.

But Muhammad, Ali, and I had not fled. Muhammad was the only one who, along with his angels, was determined to win this lost war, and I followed him everywhere he went to protect him.

In vain, he again urged his fleeing men to 'Turn around! Look at the sky! The angels are coming!'

Then Ali and I did something foolish. For a split second, we looked up at the sky as if real angels would descend. At that very moment, when we were not paying close enough attention, a man on foot suddenly appeared from behind a sandhill. It was an enemy soldier who recognized Muhammad, but he was momentarily startled by his presence on the battlefield. Then, without hesitating further, he picked up a stone and threw it at Muhammad. The stone hit Muhammad in the face and broke one of his front teeth. The man threw another stone—a large one this time—which struck Muhammad's head. He lost his balance and fell unconscious from his horse.

The soldier ran up the hill and cried out hysterically, 'Muhammad. Muhammad. I've killed Muhammad.'

Ali did not waste any time. He struck the man down with his sword, and to mislead the enemy set off galloping in the direction of Medina, with three riders in pursuit.

This gave me time to hide Muhammad. I dragged him across the ground to a safe spot. I cut off his long braids with my sword, pulled off his costly army boots so he was barefoot and would not be recognized as a leader. I then hid him behind some bushes. Afterwards, I jumped on my horse and took up position nearby, where there was a clump of trees. Still seated in my saddle, I concealed myself behind those trees and kept watch over Muhammad from afar.

Once it got dark, I returned to him. I placed Muhammad on my horse and rode to Medina, directly to the house of his personal physician.

Then I went to look for Abu Bakr. I rode back to the hills just outside the city, where the men who had fled were ready and waiting in the event of an enemy attack on the city.

Ali had warned Abu Bakr that Muhammad had been wounded. The enemy had spread the rumour that Muhammad was dead. Uthman and Ali had looked everywhere for us but with no success. The air was filled with despair, and one sensed that everybody had lost the courage to keep up the fight.

I found Abu Bakr with a group of the clan chieftains. Clearly, he had not expected to see me alive again. He immediately inquired about Muhammad. I rode up to him, leaned over, brought my head to his ear, and whispered, 'Muhammad is alive, but he's seriously injured.'

'Where is he?'

'In Medina.'

'Umar!' Abu Bakr called out.

Umar appeared and threw me a questioning glance. Abu Bakr whispered the news in Umar's ear.

Umar jumped on his horse and rode as fast as he could to the fighters, 'Long live Muhammad! He's in Medina. Unite! Defend the city! Defend your wives and your children! Defend your homes and your fields!'

All the men waved their swords in the air and let out a cry in unison, 'Long live Muhammad!' Nothing would stop them now.

75 The Jews

After his victory, Abu Sufyan, the military commander of Mecca, decided to attack Medina and conquer the city. But he soon received the news that Muhammad was not dead and that the army, under Umar's leadership, had taken up position in front of the city gate. Moreover, the clan chieftains had ordered the population to fight under Umar and defend the city inside its walls. The men wielded their swords at the crossings. The women and children climbed up on the rooftops with their bows and arrows and stones to battle the Meccan army. Mecca would never take Medina.

Abu Sufyan considered his options and was afraid he would lose a war fought inside Medina's walls. Would it not be better to stop while he was ahead and return at a later date with a larger army?

The people of Medina waited with baited breath for his attack but to everybody's amazement, Abu Sufyan decided to retreat to Mecca.

I, Zayd, must have talked to everybody about this, but I never managed to find out why he did not attack Medina. He knew from his spies that Muhammad had been wounded and was out of commission for the time being. Abu Sufyan had inflicted heavy damages on Muhammad's army, so why did he not push forward? Was he really afraid that a battle within Medina's walls would fail so miserably?

It is possible that the fear of complete humiliation discouraged Abu Sufyan from invading Medina. Imagine the loss of face for Mecca if the population of Medina had wiped out Abu Sufyan's army, and not a single soldier managed to flee the city to bring the news of the defeat back to Mecca.

Perhaps that was the reason Abu Sufyan returned to Mecca with his army.

Things calmed down in the few months Muhammad was recuperating. He knew Mecca was secretly working on a plan to invade Medina. He was aware of the situation but confident it would take some time before they attacked the city.

Before it came to that, Muhammad had another matter he needed to deal with: the Jews.

Muhammad, who had grown to hate the Jews because they conspired with the Meccan army, realized that as long as there were Jews in Medina, he could not win the war. He waited for a chance to solve the problem of the Jews, once and for all.

His uncle Abbas had harshly criticized him in the past about his agreement with the Jews, 'That was a stupid move, Muhammad. The Jews have deceived you. What were you thinking, choosing Jerusalem? If you want the support of Mecca's powerful merchants, you must choose the Kaaba, not the sanctuary of the Jews. Never turn your back on Mecca. Mecca signifies trade, and the Kaaba signifies power. Revoke your decision! Face the Kaaba, Muhammad!'

The time had now come to break his promise to the Jews.

'The Jews have betrayed us. They've passed secret information about our army to the Meccans,' was the word on the street in Medina. The constant arguing that took place erupted into heated discussions and scuffles between the Arabs and the Jews.

At the bazaar, a Jewish man expressed his affection for an Arab woman. She wanted nothing of it and called on the Arab men to defend her honour. The Arabs and the Jews came to blows. The conflict got out of hand, and they beat one another bloody, resulting in the death of an Arab.

Allah promptly reacted, revealing the command Muhammad needed, 'Muhammad! Tear up your agreement with the Jews. You do not have to keep your word! They are traitors; a Jew is nothing but a traitor.'

Muhammad tore up the agreement and pressured the Jews to deliver the perpetrator. They refused, but the leader of the Jewish Banu Nadir tribe invited Muhammad to discuss the issue. Muhammad accepted the invitation and went. But they had devised a plan to kill him. Muhammad discovered this in time and managed to escape.

Muhammad's patience with the Jews had run out, and he took the decision he had wanted to take for the longest time. He gave the Jews twenty-four hours to leave the city. Each family was allowed to take as many possessions a camel could carry. However, they had to leave their gold and money behind.

The Jews ignored the order, retreated behind the walls of their neighbourhood, and locked the gate. Muhammad waited for a week, but they stayed put in their homes and did not leave the city as ordered.

'The longer you resist, the harsher the punishment will be. Now three families have to load all their belongings onto one camel.'

Once again, the Jews did not obey, and they succeeded in holding out for two more weeks.

Then Muhammad did something he should not have done. He had all their date palms set on fire, which also laid waste to their fields. This caused the Jews such sorrow that it broke their resistance.

'Leave at once, or I will also burn your houses to the ground, and this time you're not allowed to take anything with you. That is Allah's new command.'

The Jews no longer had a choice. They destroyed their own homes: they pulled the windows out of the walls and smashed their possessions to bits, so that nothing would be left for Muhammad's supporters. Then, the Jews departed their city with empty hands.

But during this mass departure, their wives pounded drums and everybody cheered, to show Muhammad he could not break their spirits.

Now that Medina was completely in Muhammad's hands, he also decided to eliminate the Jews from the surrounding villages. Though first he corrected two of his earlier decisions for all eternity:

'Mecca is more important than Jerusalem: from now on we shall change direction and face the Kaaba when we pray. And we shall no longer fast with the Jews.'

Then he called on all the Arabs of the city to unite under his green flag.

The people cheered. The shopkeepers shut their shops for the day, and everybody rallied behind Muhammad.

76 Amr ibn Jihash, the Old Rabbi

I went looking for a former Jewish resident of Medina, to see what he might have to say. Now that Islam had conquered half the world, not a single Jew dared to talk to me.

In the village of Khaybar, I found a famous rabbi who had once lived in Yathrib. His name was Amr ibn Jihash and he had reached the impressive age of ninety. He walked with a stoop but reasonably well, and his mind was still sharp.

He lived alone in a simple room in his eldest son's house. His possessions consisted of a jug to fetch drinking water, a hard loaf of bread, a bowl of fresh dates, and the rug on which he sat and slept.

He was not afraid of anybody. Still, I started by assuring him that I would not tell anyone about our conversation and that nobody would read about it either.

He agreed to talk to me, surprisingly enough under the condition that his story be included in my book without any changes and that his name be mentioned explicitly. I swore by the Qur'an that I would honour his wishes.

Then we walked through Khaybar's legendary citadel, the 'Fortress of the Jews', out into the fields.

I have quoted Amir ibn Jihash word for word:

'I've spent my whole life in synagogues and have read almost all the ancient books, but no prophet ever used as much violence as your Muhammad. Except for the Pharaohs, no figure in history has caused the Jews as much suffering as Muhammad.

'Of course we couldn't accept that illiterate locust eater as a prophet. He ravished young women and thought up suras to justify eliminating us.

'At first we saw him as an ambitious rebel and later as an ambitious tribe chieftain. Initially we were able to sit at a table with him to try and reach a compromise, but when he started behaving like a present-day Musa, problems arose.

'When we finally saw him for the ruthless leader he was, naturally we went looking for allies to undermine him. For centuries, we were the ones who wielded power in Yathrib and controlled the marketplaces. Once he took over the city, he did everything he could to drive us out. Eventually, he got his way and banished us with our wives and children beyond the city gate. He stole all our possessions, even our children's shoes. He razed my beloved village Khaybar to the ground and burnt all the date palms and fields.

'We knew he was untrustworthy, yet we underestimated his appeal. He was extraordinary, but we didn't realize that at the time.

'Later, all the Jews united and attacked him. With no result. He won. Later we joined forces with the Meccan army against him. Again to no avail. He won.

'When he conquered the entire realm, there was no other way. We were forced to accept that Muhammad was a messenger, that Allah was the new God, and that the Qur'an was the new Holy Book.

'He joined the line of the ancient prophets using force and went as far as declaring himself the last prophet on earth.

'How clever of your Muhammad to fill more than half his Book with stories from our Torah, yet he curses the Jews throughout his Qur'an.

'I have one foot in my grave, so I'm not afraid to say what

I think. Put the following in your book for future generations, "When you read this, Amr ibn Jihash will be long dead in his grave, but from his final resting place his voice cries out, 'Muhammad was no messenger. He was the prophet of thieves!'"

77 Aisha, Muhammad's Favourite Wife

Medina was quiet again. Muhammad was safe. For the time being, satisfied with the gold he had stolen from the Jews, he left the caravan routes alone.

To give you an impression of his life in that quiet period, I shall let the old servant of his favourite wife, the young Aisha, speak. Her name is Bayt Kulthum, and she must be in her sixties by now.

'Kulthum, tell me something special about those days,' I said.

'Something special?' Kulthum reacted smiling. 'I don't know what to say. Let me think back. I was always with Aisha; I was something of a second mother to her. That's what Muhammad wanted. I gave her guidance when Muhammad began sharing her bed. I taught her how a woman should behave. That's why I was honoured with the title Bayt Kulthum, "Mother of the House".

'Yes, I have a few stories I can tell you. I was in my room and through the window I saw Muhammad and Aisha strolling in the courtyard. Muhammad was crazy about her. He always gave in to Aisha's wishes. He was well over fifty; she was fourteen years old. He was joking around with her, pulling her red hair, teasing her, and running away, and Aisha was playfully chasing after him. He was still agile and strong. Aisha jumped on his back, bit his ear, and pushed him to the ground. Muhammad knelt, holding his ear from the pain, and Aisha giggled and flirtatiously dared him to catch her.

'Then another time, Aisha heard musicians on the street.

She wanted to see them. But Muhammad had just banned music. Aisha would have nothing of this edict.

'I heard Muhammad say, "Aisha! Allah has forbidden music."

'Aisha replied, "But … you're my husband."

"I can't help you. It's between you and Allah."

"But, please … you're my husband."

'Aisha ultimately got her way with Muhammad. He stooped so she could stand on his back and peak over the wall at the street musicians.'

Another anecdote popped into Kulthum's mind, 'Muhammad and Aisha were strolling along a path in the shade of the tall date palms. As usual, I was a short distance behind them. Aisha said, "I'll race you to that last tree."

'And they bolted off like two wild children. I ran after them to see how it would end. First Muhammad was ahead, but then Aisha overtook him and won. She gently patted his belly and said, "My husband has put on some weight!"

'Her victory remained a sensitive subject. Though Muhammad always smiled about her winning the race, I noticed he was eating less. A short time later, he took Aisha along to the same path and suggested, "Let's race again? To the last tree?"

'Aisha dashed off, but this time Muhammad overtook her and won.

'Then he patted her on the behind and said, "My wife has put on some weight!"'

The story Kulthum had just told me, reminded me about how much Muhammad loved to run. Whenever there were races among his men, he generally took part.

He also liked wrestling. Umar was his toughest opponent. He could never win from him.

After such a wrestling match, Muhammad would always say, 'When Umar wrestles, his body is as strong as iron. The fire of hell burns in his eyes. Only the devil can beat him.'

With a smile, Kulthum indicated there was something else she wanted to tell me. 'One time, Aisha showed me a sura from Muhammad's Qur'an that was actually a rule he created for himself. Muslim women were allowed to give themselves to the prophet if they specifically wanted to do this.

'Aisha was enraged by this text, furious at Muhammad. She couldn't sleep out of jealousy and quarrelled with him, "How good of your Allah, to help you satisfy your physical needs."'

Another favourite wife of Muhammad's was Hafsa, the twenty-four year old daughter of Umar.

'Hafsa possessed talents that Aisha didn't have,' said Kulthum. 'Hafsa could read; so could Aisha. Hafsa could write; so could Aisha. Hafsa could write poetry, but Aisha couldn't. The charming Hafsa persuaded Muhammad to work on improving his reading and writing skills, something Aisha couldn't do either.

'Aisha couldn't sit still. Whenever Muhammad came into her room, she jumped on his back.

'Hafsa, however, could sit still, and she let Muhammad lay his head on her lap while she read aloud to him.

'Aisha, who was still a child, gave Muhammad her youth and her beauty. Hafsa embroidered one of Muhammad's texts on her handkerchief with colourful threads. Aisha was green with jealousy. She always complained to me, "That witch thinks she can cast a spell on my husband with red, yellow, and green threads."'

78 The Trench

Although Muhammad was not busy making concrete plans for another war, he kept a close and constant watch on Mecca. He had plenty of people in Mecca loyal to him; they were his eyes and ears. One of them was Hamza, who rushed away from Mecca—galloping day and night to Medina—to warn Muhammad that danger was on its way. Hamza told me this story himself:

'My mother worked in Abu Sufyan's kitchen. She told me everything she overheard there, and I passed that information on to Muhammad. But no matter how hard I tried, I couldn't find out when Abu Sufyan was going to move on Medina with his army. It was a secret he kept buried deep in his heart.

'One day he left the city with an army of ten thousand men. I jumped on my horse and rode toward Medina as fast as I could. I travelled day and night, changing horses seven times.

'In Medina, I went straight to the mosque where Muhammad would most likely be for evening prayer. I quickly removed my shoes, ran to him, knelt before him exhausted, kissed him on his left shoulder, and whispered in his ear, "They're on their way with ten thousand men strong. You have eight to ten days before they arrive."'

Muhammad rose immediately.

'Zayd, alert the men!' he instructed.

I, Zayd, set off without delay to warn Abu Bakr, Umar, Uthman, and Salman Farsi.

A short time later, they all arrived in the mosque. I arranged extra candles, food, and drinks. They deliberated until late at night, discussing all sorts of possibilities.

Confronting the enemy outside the city in the mountains was not an option; given they were ten thousand men.

Shutting the gate and defending the city from its stone walls did not seem feasible either; the enemy has enough strength and means to break through our defences.

Suddenly Salman Farsi came up with a brilliant plan, an old tactic from the Persian art of warfare, 'We can dig a trench around the city to keep the enemy from advancing.'

A trench?

Nobody knew what a trench was. What did it look like?

The decision had been made. There was no time for objections.

'Summon the clan leaders,' Muhammad said to me.

In the middle of the night, I galloped to the homes of the chieftains and woke them up, 'You must come to the mosque immediately!'

One by one they arrived at the mosque on horseback.

Muhammad said to the clan chieftains, 'We need to call on all the inhabitants of the city. Men, women, children, everyone!'

The next morning, the town criers climbed up on the roofs, blew their horns, and made the announcement, 'Everybody must come to the gate with a shovel, a pickaxe, and a bucket!'

A few hours later, there were hundreds of people at the gate. Muhammad spoke to them, 'Medina is going to make history. The enemy is on their way with ten thousand men. Allah has commanded me to dig a trench around the city. Whoever helps will enjoy both the wonderful gardens of Medina as well as the delightful gardens of paradise. We have seven days and six nights. We will start immediately. Whoever leaves the city is in league with the enemy and will be struck down on the spot.'

Abu Nuwas wrote a poem especially for the occasion. He mounted his horse and recited it to the crowd:

'Medina!
You! Bride of the cities of the world.
We are going to immortalize you
With a trench.
Women of Medina!
Deny your husband in bed.
Send him off to the gateway
Of Medina.
Men! Grab your pickaxes!
Dig six long nights!
Only when you have finished,
Will women come, with cups
In their hands
And a bride in their midst,
For all eternity.'

Everybody started digging, shovelling, cooking, singing, arguing, smoking, laughing, reciting suras, and praying. In six unforgettable days and five incredible nights the trench was completed.

All of the men were standing there—in that empty deep trench—and nobody knew what was going to happen next.

Then Muhammad grabbed a shovel and with his own hands dug the ditch that would connect the trench to the river outside Medina. When the river magically flowed into the trench, everybody cheered with joy.

Abu Sufyan marched on Medina with his ten thousand soldiers. He assumed he would conquer the city in one day. He was not aware of the trench, because under Umar's leadership the city was heavily guarded, and none of Abu Sufyan's spies had managed to leave the city to warn him ahead of time.

Abu Sufyan expected to face Muhammad's army somewhere outside the city, but there was no man, no donkey, no dog, no camel to be found in the surroundings of Medina. They saw the city walls and the gate in the distance, but did not know about the trench yet.

Once they got closer, they saw that a miracle had occurred. The city was surrounded by water. They had never seen such a thing.

Medina was beyond reach.

Abu Sufyan waited on the other side of the trench for an entire week, powerless.

What could he do? Nothing.

Muhammad had won the war without any bloodshed.

79 The Treaty

It began to occur to Mecca that this was not about Muhammad alone, but about a movement that could no longer be ignored. If they wanted to safeguard trading in Mecca, there was only one way to do this. They would have to appeal to Muhammad.

Muhammad received word that Mecca wanted to make peace and responded positively. An appointment was set up for a meeting. With a small delegation, Abu Sufyan came to the town of Hudaybiyyah, which lay between Mecca and Medina.

Muhammad went with his delegation to Hudaybiyyah as well. Because they did not want to meet in someone's home, they gathered outside of town in the shade of the almond trees.

Neither of the delegations wanted to sit, so they stood, facing each other in two half circles, with some distance between them.

Sa'id ibn Jubayr, the personal scribe of Abu Sufyan, was present.

As was I, Zayd, the personal scribe of Muhammad.

We both took a seat on the ground without shaking hands. After all, we were sworn enemies.

The deliberations began. Standing, the men took turns speaking.

The delegations then withdrew to deliberate, only to return and face each other again to continue the discussions.

It was taking forever, and the situation was tense, but one

sensed that neither party wanted to go home empty-handed. They were intent on achieving some kind of a breakthrough.

After half a day of difficult negotiations an agreement was reached:

- There will be a ten-year truce.
- Muhammad will refrain from attacking the trade caravans.
- Mecca will not form any alliances against Muhammad.
- Muhammad will not form any alliances against Mecca.
- Muhammad will be allowed to visit the Kaaba with his men on holy days, but they will be prohibited from carrying any other weapon besides their own sword.
- Whenever Muhammad enters the city of Mecca with his men, the Meccans will stay inside their homes.

All hell broke loose when Muhammad went to officially initial the treaty with his signet ring. Muhammad's delegation wanted a phrase from the Qur'an written at the top of the treaty: *Bi-smi llahi ar-rahmani ar-rahim*, in the name of Allah. He is love. He gives. He forgives.

The Meccan delegation was not about to allow this. They said, 'Nowhere has it been proven that your Allah gives and forgives.'

After a lengthy, almost violent debate, the phrase was stripped down to, '*Bi-smi Rabbi-ka*, in the name of the Maker.'

But the disagreement did not end there. The heated discussion that followed was about Muhammad's signet ring. It read: 'Muhammad, the messenger of Allah.'

However, the Meccan delegation did not acknowledge Muhammad as the messenger. They wanted Muhammad to sign with his official name: Muhammad ibn Abdullah,

Muhammad the son of Abdullah.

To the great displeasure of his own delegation, Muhammad agreed and signed as Muhammad ibn Abdullah.

Only then did Muhammad and Abu Sufyan shake hands.

We, the scribes, also shook hands with each other.

The members of both delegations did the same, although they were clearly ill at ease with one another.

Muhammad's delegates were angry with him because had compromised too much, but he said, 'Have patience. Allah asked me to arrange this settlement. I know nothing. He is all-knowing.'

Then, in high spirits, we triumphantly rode back to Medina.

80 Muhammad Becomes Untouchable

A week later, Muhammad called me into his room. He closed the door and said, 'Take your horse and ride to the Kingdom of Habasha. Don't stop on the way.'

With my head bowed, I listened attentively to what he was saying.

'Tell nobody about your orders. Once you've reached your destination, find Abu Sufyan's daughter.'

Habiba, the young daughter of Abu Sufyan, lived in neighbouring Habasha. Recently widowed, she had been left alone with three small children.

Muhammad placed a necklace—a rainbow of precious gems—in the palm of my hand and said, 'Ask for Habiba's hand in marriage for the messenger of Allah. It must be arranged quickly. Don't give her a chance to say no.'

I knew Muhammad better than myself, so I was never surprised by the unexpected tasks I received from him. I immediately saddled my horse and departed. I travelled a long time before reaching the city where she lived. I asked around and found Habiba in a large stone house behind the marketplace. Her servant opened the door.

'I'm an emissary from Medina. I've come with a message for Habiba, the daughter of Abu Sufyan.'

She looked me up and down. My face and shoulders were still covered with sand from my journey, and my horse was thirsty. She had a servant lead my horse to the stable. I was given a cup of water and asked to wait outside in the courtyard.

It did not take long before an attractive young woman

appeared at the door, with three small children trailing behind. I immediately knew it was Habiba because of the resemblance to her father.

I bowed slightly, 'Zayd is my name. I'm the emissary of Muhammad the messenger.'

Her handmaiden was watching us from a distance away, and her other servants were looking on from behind the windows.

'I have a message for you that I can only discuss in private.'

She took me to the room where she received guests. I handed her the necklace and said, 'I have been sent by the messenger to ask for your hand in marriage,' and I gave her a personal letter from Muhammad. The daughter of Mecca's most powerful man knew how to conduct herself. She immediately understood what this was about.

She read the letter and gazed out the window.

Abu Sufyan's daughter was not only beautiful, she was smart as well. I did not need to tell her much more. She had undoubtedly heard the rumours of a peace agreement between Muhammad and her father.

'How much time do I have to think about this?' she asked.

'Little, if any,' I said, 'if you agree, I shall make immediate arrangements for us to leave first thing in the morning. Nobody knows about this.'

She went off by herself to think in the courtyard.

Habiba understood she had to make the decision alone, that it had to happen immediately, and that it should remain a secret until she reached Medina—until she entered Muhammad's house.

What was she thinking? I went to the window and followed her with my eyes.

Her resolve demonstrated that she was truly Abu Sufyan's

daughter. As she came back into the house, her answer sparkled around her neck. She was wearing Muhammad's necklace.

Still I asked the question officially, 'Do you accept the proposal of marriage from Muhammad the messenger?'

'I accept,' she said.

I recited a short sura from the Qur'an to bless her betrothal to Muhammad.

The next day, we left for Medina with her children and servants loaded onto seven camels.

When our small caravan entered the city through the gateway, nobody knew who she was, or what her presence would mean.

Habiba and her children were immediately brought to Muhammad's house. He welcomed them and with his bare hands wiped the dust from his bride's shoes, while she was still seated on the saddled camel.

Then a public announcement was made.

Abu Sufyan received the news as well.

His great enemy Muhammad had become his son-in-law and a member of their clan. Now, nobody would dare lay a hand on Muhammad in Mecca without Abu Sufyan's personal consent.

81 Hafsa, the Rival of Aisha

Muhammad was already known throughout the realm. but the miraculous victory he achieved with his cunning trench brought him even greater fame. He had won a war against the Meccan army without even lifting his sword.

Moreover, he had succeeded in getting Abu Sufyan's daughter to share his bed.

Even if Muhammad could not perform miracles the way Musa and Isa had, he had become something of a miracle himself.

He seemed untouchable. He kept a close eye on everything and discussed everything with his advisers down to the smallest details, to limit any potential damage.

Because he was so focused on Mecca, he barely had time for Aisha. He did not see that he had awakened Aisha's venomous jealousy by sharing his bed with the beautiful Habiba.

He had also forgotten that the poets of Mecca, who were masters of mockery, had been waiting years for an incident to belittle him.

They sought. They found.

Muhammad, who had reached a solid compromise with Mecca, now had his hands free to crush the rest of the opposition, such as that of the Jews in the villages between Medina and Mecca.

Each time Muhammad left Medina with his army, he always took one of his wives along.

When it was Aisha's turn to accompany him, something

happened that would have far-reaching consequences for the women of the world.

Nobody is better qualified to tell this story than Hafsa, because she experienced it first-hand. She was the daughter of Umar, and Muhammad's second young beloved wife.

Hafsa and Aisha were each other's rivals.

Once, after they were both widowed by Muhammad, I visited Hafsa. She received me in her enchanting sitting room, where she was surrounded by seven maids. One lit her water pipe, another brought her a cup of tea on a gold tray, and yet another spoiled her with sweets.

'Aisha was calculating, and she still is,' Hafsa said. 'In those days she acted as if Muhammad had only one wife, and of course it was her. Today she behaves like she's Muhammad's only widow. She pretends to be the queen of the realm. Look at how she lives—she rides around on an elephant.

'Let her play queen of the world, but let none forget the story I'm going to tell you.

'Muhammad was about to leave with his army again. This time his old wife Salama was supposed to accompany him. But Aisha bribed her with a necklace and went in her place.

'Aisha was a sly one; nobody could have imagined that she kept a lover on the side. What possesses you to do such a thing when you're the wife of the messenger? But she did have a lover, and, unfortunately, Muhammad defended her.

'When the battle was over, and they were all on their way home, they stopped somewhere in the desert to rest for the afternoon. Aisha secretly withdrew from the group; she hid behind a sand dune and waited until everybody was gone. Only when the army was back in Medina, was Aisha missed. They went looking for her everywhere but with no success.

Poor Muhammad thought his beautiful red-haired wife had been abducted by the defeated Jews. But the Jews assured him that they hadn't taken her.

'The next day at sunrise, Aisha appeared on a camel at the gate to Medina.

'Who did the camel belong to? To the handsome young warlord Safwan.'

I, Zayd, remember this as if it were yesterday. Poor Muhammad felt powerless when this was reported to him.

He attempted to limit the damage, but it was too late; the poets had already sharpened their pencils, and Muhammad's enemies quickly spread the satirical verses throughout the land:

'Where is Aisha?
Behind the sand dune.
What is she doing there?
We don't know.
Only Muhammad's Allah knows.
For He is all-knowing!'

82 The Headscarf

Muhammad brought Aisha home and locked the door. They began to argue—all hell broke loose in the house.

Kulthum, Aisha's trusted servant, heard everything. Crying, Aisha said she was free of all blame.

'Where were you?' shouted Muhammad upset.

'I needed to go to the sand dune,' Aisha replied, still crying.

'Why didn't you return when we were packing up to leave?'

'I came back, but then I realized the precious necklace you gave me wasn't around my neck. When I was looking for it I lost track of the time, and when I returned all of you were gone.'

'You're lying!' shouted Muhammad.

'I'm not lying! 'I'm not lying! I don't lie! shouted Aisha, and she began hitting herself.

Muhammad loved her; he could not bear her pain.

'What am I supposed to tell people now?'

'Allah knows I'm innocent,' she answered angrily.

'Go wash your face! I have to think about what I should say,' Muhammad replied exhausted.

'You're my husband, the messenger. You can do whatever you want.'

And that ended the argument.

But Muhammad could not quiet the mouths of the poets. The pressure increased. Even the warlords displayed their dissatisfaction. Ali revealed that he was not satisfied with Aisha's explanation, and Umar and Uthman suggested he send Aisha home to her parents for a while.

Muhammad had no choice. He reluctantly followed their advice.

Peace and quiet returned for a time. Although according to Hafsa it did not last very long.

'Muhammad had sent Aisha to the house of her father, Abu Bakr. Muhammad then shared my bed,' Hafsa said, 'but he couldn't sleep. All he talked about the entire night was Aisha. He loved her; cried in my bed.

'He cursed the poets. He said that they were fools. He left my side at dawn.'

Muhammad rushed to Abu Bakr's house. He knocked on the door, and Kulthum opened it.

'I need to see Aisha,' he shouted.

Again there was a harsh exchange of words between him and his young wife. Then Aisha began to weep softly and to complain, 'Muhammad the messenger chooses to listen to the snitches. Look at how much weight I've lost. I'm skin and bones. I'm no longer pretty. My face is pale—and not because of the poets, but because of my husband.

'He'll be the death of me.

'He knows I'm innocent, but he does nothing.'

Muhammad began to shake; he started to babble out of control. Aisha recognized these moments; she knew he was receiving a new revelation from Allah. She immediately stood up, grabbed a blanket, draped it around his head and shoulders, and helped him into bed. Muhammad was writhing under the blanket; he was babbling. He was talking to Allah. It took a while for him to receive the message. Then he fell into a deep sleep.

Aisha pushed the blanket aside. Sweat was dripping from Muhammad's face and trickling down his neck. She wiped it with the hem of her dress and kissed him on the forehead. Allah had instructed Muhammad to take Aisha home.

I transcribed that sura:

> 'Those who accuse decent married women of adultery and do not come forward with four witnesses are to receive eighty lashes. You must not accept their testimony in the future. They are at fault.
>
> 'Those who accuse decent women, who know no evil, of debauchery shall be cursed in this life and in the life hereafter. A severe punishment awaits them.
>
> 'On a given day, their tongue, hands, and feet shall testify to what they have done. On that day, God shall determine what they deserve, and they shall understand that Allah knows the truth.
>
> 'Muhammad, tell male believers that they should lower their eyes and preserve their chastity. Such is pure for them. Allah knows all things.
>
> 'And tell female believers that they should lower their eyes and preserve their chastity; that they should not expose more of their adornment than is naturally visible; that they should drape their veils over their breasts; and that they should expose their adornment to no one but their husbands, their fathers, their sons, the sons of their husbands, their brothers, the sons of their brothers, the sons of their sisters, the women of their own faith, their male servants who have no need of women, and children who pay no attention as yet to the female body.
>
> 'Muhammad, tell the women that they must not stamp hard on the ground with their feet, lest the hidden adornment of their feet be exposed.'

Hereafter, women appearing in public had to wear headscarves and were only allowed to share their beauty with their husbands.

From that time forward, people started to fit their homes with door knockers. When the women heard a knock at the door, they disappeared into the back rooms.

83 Marching on Mecca

After this clear directive from Allah about Aisha, the gossip died down. As an example, to enforce the new laws, two poets were punished in public with eighty lashes for spreading new satirical poems. What's more, it was restless in Medina. Every day something new happened, and people did not have time to focus on Aisha any longer. Muhammad had agreed to a ten-year truce with Mecca, but only I, Zayd, and Allah knew about the diabolical plan Muhammad had in mind.

Daily, from all over the realm, dozens of young men arrived, alone or in groups, to volunteer for Muhammad's army. One by one, Muhammad attacked all the Jewish villages between Medina and Mecca. He disarmed the Jewish men and took their confiscated weapons back to Medina.

Two years later, Muhammad tore up the agreement with Mecca and without warning advanced on the city with fifty thousand men.

Besides his advisers, nobody knew where he was going with his army at that moment—they wanted to keep it a secret as long as possible.

The sun had just risen when Muhammad went and stood on a hill outside Medina to address his army, 'You're not the one who shoots an arrow. It is God who shoots. You're not the one who kills them. God kills them.'

It was a message he had received from Allah the night before. He cried, 'Allah fights with us.'

All his men cheered and raised their swords in the air.

Abu Sufyan received an urgent message from his allies in Medina that Muhammad was on his way with a large army. It was the holy month of Ramadan. Abu Sufyan had taken just about everything into account but not a war and certainly not Muhammad marching on Mecca unexpectedly. Up until then, Muhammad had strictly adhered to the stipulations of the peace agreement. He no longer attacked the caravans and even visited Mecca once with a group of his followers. In addition, Abu Sufyan and Muhammad had met regularly over the past two years and had even eaten together and talked. This was after Muhammad married his daughter.

Yet there was no doubt about it: Muhammad could only be heading to one place and that was Mecca.

I, Zayd, followed Muhammad on my horse. We were now close to Mecca, and the army stopped a safe distance from the city wall, where the arrows could not reach us.

This would be an all-important battle. Muhammad had completely eradicated the power base of the Jews. Still, they were always a topic of discussion. For the time being, they could not rise up against him, but if Muhammad lost the war against Mecca, they might join forces with his enemies to conquer Medina.

Muhammad had to win this time; he had no other option. He was even willing to destroy Mecca if necessary.

The Meccans were shocked by the unexpected presence of an army at the city gate. Everyone hurried home frightened and locked their doors. The people knew what they had done to Muhammad and what awaited them if he invaded the city. They knew it was not beyond him to set the city ablaze as an act of revenge.

Muhammad's first goal was to conquer the city without any fighting. He was counting on Abu Sufyan for this, because Habiba had tried to forge a fragile friendship between her husband and her father, and she was a trusted envoy between these two headstrong men.

She always took Muhammad's greetings to her father whenever she went to Mecca to visit her family and conveyed her father's greetings to Muhammad when she returned to Medina.

Now Muhammad and his army were suddenly at Mecca's gate. And Abu Sufyan could feel Muhammad's sword in his neck.

Muhammad had sent Ali ahead to Mecca to contact his uncle Abbas and ask him to mediate with Abu Sufyan.

Years later, Ali recalled that day:

'I entered Mecca disguised as a merchant. I was instructed to knock on Abbas' door when Muhammad's army reached the gate to Mecca, not before.

'Once Muhammad had arrived, I walked along the streets of Mecca. The powerful merchants were fleeing the city. The slave owners had left their fields and farm land in the care of their slaves and taken refuge in the mountain caves.

'Everybody barricaded themselves in their homes and nailed their doors shut from inside. The shopkeepers loaded their wares onto camels and took everything to their homes for safekeeping. They knew that if the army took the city, Muhammad's followers would plunder all the shops.

'It was total chaos. I had never seen Mecca in such a state. The people were paralyzed with fear. Where was their fighting spirit?

'I calmly walked to Abbas' house and knocked. His servant

opened the door a crack and asked what I wanted. I said I was an emissary from Medina, and I wanted to speak to Abbas in person. The man looked frightened when he heard the word "Medina". He shut the door and left me waiting outside.

'A moment later the door opened again. This time it was Abbas himself. I greeted him, he recognized me, took me inside, and I immediately related the following, "Muhammad asks you to act as Allah's mediator and to talk to Abu Sufyan. Muhammad demands that Abu Sufyan leave the city on foot to meet with him. That is the message I bring. I have nothing more to add."

'Abbas put on his coat and shouted, "My horse!"'

84 The Kaaba

The army was now ready and waiting for Muhammad's order to attack.

Except for Abu Bakr, Umar, Uthman, Ali, and I, nobody knew that Muhammad had sent his uncle Abbas to Abu Sufyan as a mediator.

The city gate was shut, and I saw Muhammad could not keep his eyes off of it. On the walls were Meccan soldiers. They had their bows and arrows pointed at us.

The unshakable Umar and Uthman were in charge of preparations for battle. Carpenters constructed ladders that the fighters would soon use to climb over the walls and enter the city. Strong men had felled large date palms to be used as battering rams to demolish the city gate. The camels and horses were positioned behind the front line. The troops prepared themselves for fighting in the streets.

Since it was the holy fasting month of Ramadan, Muhammad had decided to make an exception. He ordered his soldiers to eat and drink well.

Muhammad waited.

I waited.

Muhammad kept staring at the gate.

Abu Sufyan appeared, he took a few steps forward and then stopped. Abbas also came through the gate, walked to Abu Sufyan, and stood beside him.

Muhammad shouted, 'Take up position!'

The army assembled. Muhammad gestured to me. I urged my horse forward and brought my ear to his lips.

Then I galloped to Umar, leaned over, and whispered, 'Go to Abu Sufyan! Greet him like a king, and escort him to Muhammad's tent.'

Umar grabbed the green army flag, held it high in the air, and with a group of men approached Abu Sufyan on horseback. When he was near to him, he dismounted and walked toward Abu Sufyan, still holding the flag in the air. He lowered the flag slightly—it was an invitation to meet with Muhammad. Abu Sufyan followed Umar while the horsemen accompanied them in a stately fashion.

Umar shouted, 'Lower your arrows!'

The army pointed their weapons at the ground.

Muhammad welcomed Abu Sufyan in front of his white tent and invited him inside. Then, I pulled the tent curtain closed behind them.

After a brief conversation, Muhammad appeared in front of the tent again and said, 'Fetch my camel!'

Muhammad rode this white camel during festivities in Medina. The camel had a sweet face, walked with dignity, and exuded calm. I made the animal kneel at Abu Sufyan's feet. He went and sat in the saddle, and I made the camel rise.

In this honourable way, Abu Sufyan returned to the city.

Ali was near the gate at that moment. He could see everything and was waiting for what was to come.

Ali recounted, 'The Meccans, who had closed down their shops on the bazaar and taken refuge in their homes, kept a close eye on the city from behind their windows. Nothing moved in the streets—people even demanded silence from their dogs and cats.

'When I saw Abu Sufyan entering the city on Muhammad's

white camel, I couldn't believe my eyes. Did this mean that Muhammad had conquered the city? Was the camel actually the symbol of victory? I ducked into an alley as Abu Sufyan went by. I couldn't tell anything from his demeanour. Once he'd passed me, I followed him at a distance. The people gazed at him from behind their windows. He rode straight to his house, went inside, and shut the door.'

I, Zayd, can still see Muhammad's heralds with their copper bullhorns riding into the city on their camels and announcing:

'Whoever remains at home is safe.
Whoever has taken refuge in Abu Sufyan's house will be pardoned.
Whoever goes outside shall be slain.
Everyone is to stay inside until further notice!'

Muhammad then rode his horse into the city and his army followed behind in three columns.

The first column, led by Abu Bakr, followed Muhammad and went straight ahead to the Kaaba Square.

The second column was led by Umar and took the road to the Kaaba Square on the right.

The third column was led by Uthman and took the road to the Kaaba Square on the left.

When all three columns were reunited on the square, Muhammad dismounted and entered the Kaaba with his sword in hand.

I followed right behind him, with a long coil of sturdy rope thrown over my right shoulder.

Muhammad approached al-'Uzza, the chief idol of Mecca. He threw the rope around the neck of the great stone goddess and pulled her down: al-'Uzza broke into pieces, the floor shook; offerings, lanterns, and torches fell to the ground.

Muhammad did not destroy the largest idol, Hubal. Later, when he built the first mosque in Mecca, he gave orders for the idol Hubal to be buried in front of the door so that everyone entering the mosque would walk over it.

Muhammad went outside and gestured to Bilal, the orator. Bilal leaned a ladder against a wall of the Kaaba, climbed onto the roof, and proclaimed:

'La 'ilaha 'illa llah
Muhammadan rasulu llah!'

Under Umar's leadership, thirty-five strong men wielding sledgehammers went into the Kaaba. They destroyed the other idols, brought the bits and pieces to the square, and threw them onto a heap. All the gold and jewellery was put into large bags, loaded on camels, and taken to the former home of Abu Bakr for safekeeping. The sun had just set behind the mountains when they were finished emptying the Kaaba.

Muhammad went and stood above the crowd and exclaimed:

'The Kaaba is the House of Allah!'

He gave the order to honour it.

Fifteen thousand men walked around the Kaaba seven times, chanting:

'Labbay-ka llahumma labbay-ka
Wahda-hu wahda-hu wahda-hu wahida!'

During the night, dozens of men were taken from their homes and killed immediately. They were the ones who had blood on their hands and could under no circumstances be pardoned. Muhammad stayed in Mecca for fifteen days. Then he put Abu Bakr in charge of the city and returned to Medina.

85 The Qur'an and the Sword

I was no longer the Zayd I had once been.

I no longer sat on the floor to write. I had become the chronicler of Allah's Empire.

In Medina's mosque, a separate room was set up for me where there was a desk with my goose feather quills and ink-well. There were also all kinds of rolls of paper and parchment in a cupboard. I had decorated the walls myself with Qur'an texts, which I had written on large pieces of white cloth.

The days of having only one pair of shoes, which I wore until the soles fell off, were over. Now I had many pairs of shoes and several coats, which I would wear depending on the occasion.

I read more books than ever before because now I could get any book my heart desired.

I did not do this for myself but for Muhammad, because he was the most powerful man in the realm, and I knew that one day he would become the most powerful man in the world.

Certainly, a leader such as this deserved a distinguished, learned chronicler.

Muhammad visited my study regularly.

Then one time he said, 'Lock the door.'

I locked the door. I understood that he wanted me to write an important letter for him.

'Three letters with the same content,' he said.

'The length of the text?' I asked.

'A short letter,' he replied.

'What type of paper?'

'Special paper,' he said.

I cut three pieces of creamy white paper off a roll from China. I grabbed my finest quill pen and looked at Muhammad, ready to write down his words.

He dictated, I wrote:

From the messenger of Allah
To King Parviz of the Persian Empire

In the name of Allah
I ask the Persian King to accept Islam.
If he accepts, he will be safe.
If he does not accept, he is personally responsible for the consequences.

Signed,
Muhammad the messenger

When the great Persian king read Muhammad's letter, he tore it into pieces and threw it on the ground. Then he sent away Muhammad's courier empty-handed.

Seven years later, wielding his sword in the air and with thousands of soldiers under his command, Umar attacked the Persian Empire. His men plundered the king's palaces, and Umar set them on fire with his own hand.

The attack was so sudden and so violent that Parviz had no time to react. He mounted his horse and escaped to the eastern borders of his empire. In the evening, totally exhausted, he knocked at the door of a watermill, asking if he could spend the night.

The miller did not know who he was and beheaded him that same night for his expensive coat.

The second letter went to Heraclius, emperor of the Byzantine Empire.

When the Emperor read the letter, he personally beheaded the courier. Muhammad advanced on the Byzantine Empire with his army but was defeated.

He did not go any further. Regrouping for another attack seemed fruitless, and by retreating with his troops he managed to limit the damage.

The third letter was sent to King Najashi of neighbouring Habasha.

He accepted Islam and sent gold, unusual fragrant herbs, elegant fabric, and two extraordinarily beautiful slave girls to Muhammad.

These two beautiful women were called Mariyah and Sirin.

Muhammad bedded both of them on the same night.

86 The Night Journey

Things were going well for Muhammad. He shined like the sun during the day; at night he was as bright as the moon. He managed to unite all the clans in the country under his green flag. The time had come for Muhammad to visit Allah, to discuss the plan for the world together with Him.

I heard the rumours for the first time on the market.

'Muhammad has travelled through heaven.'

'What?'

'He met Allah on the seventh level of heaven.'

'Who told you that?'

'That's all everybody is talking about. Everyone knows about his night journey.'

I, Zayd, knew nothing about his visit to Allah. Muhammad had never mentioned this night journey in my presence.

The people even knew what Allah had told Muhammad and what commands he received:

'Muhammad! Attack the Persian Empire. Free the Persians from their corrupt kings. Destroy their false belief in Zarathustra, and reduce their fire temples to rubble. There is only one God: Allah!'

At that time, I did not know anything more about his night journey, but later I transcribed the story in the Qur'an:

'Glory be to Him. He who carried His servant by night from the Sacred Mosque to the Furthest Mosque, across the heavens.'

I, Zayd, am merely a *katib*, a scribe, a chronicler, and should probably refrain from offering my own opinion. Though this time, for my future readers, it should be clear where I got my information.

It is hard to establish if it was Muhammad who first told the story of his remarkable journey, or if the people on the street invented this journey for him. But I have my own version of the night journey, which I only heard later on from Muhammad.

It was after the conquest of Mecca. We were in Medina at Muhammad's house, standing in the courtyard. Suddenly Aisha appeared with her handmaiden. She walked right up to Muhammad and said, 'Why does everybody know, except for me? Why do I hear these things from others on the market? Am I not the wife of the messenger?'

'I didn't know ahead of time either. I never know what Allah is planning. He knows all things, and I know nothing,' Muhammad said, smiling, 'but I'll tell you something that nobody knows.'

I, Zayd, could not tell if he was serious, or he was just teasing Aisha to amuse her.

'I was alone in bed, thinking,' Muhammad said,' with my eyes closed. Suddenly I heard my name being called. I was being invited to visit Allah. I had not even recovered from the feeling of joy I felt, when a white winged horse appeared. I mounted its saddle and the horse flew with unbelievable speed through the sky. We passed the moon and other planets I had never seen. I felt the horse flying through the different tiers of heaven. When we reached the seventh level, the horse stopped in front of a majestic archway. I dismounted and entered a vast, breathtakingly beautiful garden with old trees, strange fragrant flowers, magical waterfalls, mysterious birds, golden flies, silvery butterflies, red ants, elegant cats with shiny green eyes, and large deer with impressive antlers. Beautiful girls carrying jugs of wine strolled past me. Was I in paradise? Or was I in Allah's courtyard? At that moment, I heard footsteps approaching on a path behind the trees that was paved with gold. Could it be Allah?'

'And then?' Aisha asked, amazed.

'The rest is something that took place between Allah and His messenger,' Muhammad said seriously.

'Fine, but how beautiful were the girls in Allah's garden?' Aisha asked apprehensively.

'Beautiful, exceptionally beautiful, but none of them were prettier than my Aisha.'

Later Muhammad came up with another version of his journey. I included that one in the Qur'an under the title 'The Star':

'In the name of Allah
He is love
He gives
He forgives

By the star at the moment it falls,
Your fellow human being Muhammad has not gone astray and has not been misled.
And he does not speak what he desires.
And it is nothing other than a clear revelation.
The angel Jabra'il taught it to him.

Allah is resolute. He possesses power.
He stood on the farthest horizon.
He came closer, and He descended.
To a distance of two bows or less.
He revealed to Muhammad what he had to reveal.
His heart did not lie over what he has seen.'

87 Hassan and Husayn, the Grandsons of Muhammad

Muhammad was happier and more powerful than ever. But I saw something that others had not yet noticed. Muhammad had aged—all of a sudden. It was as if he had no time to grow old before conquering Mecca, so he had waited until he had triumphed over the city.

It first struck me when he was mounting his saddled horse to return to Medina. During the journey through the desert, he was very quiet. I kept a close watch over him, he rode slumped over, seemed distracted. After the conquest of Mecca, it was as if life had lost its purpose.

Sometimes he forgot everything, he forgot his Allah, his Qur'an, his Mecca, his army, his beautiful wives, and he only thought about his two grandsons, Hassan and Husayn—the sons of his beloved daughter Fatima, who was married to Ali.

A delegation of Mecca's powerful merchants had just arrived in Medina. They were going to meet with Muhammad in the mosque to talk about implementing a tax on big trading deals.

Muhammad was up front on his horse, with the traders in their regal attire, on their regal horses, following closely behind. We rode toward the mosque. Along the way, I noticed that Muhammad had changed direction unannounced. I thought he was taking a detour to the mosque via the market square because he wanted to show his guests all the new developments in the centre of the city. However, he avoided the centre and kept going. I wanted to ask him where he was heading, but

I went along without questioning him.

The delegation followed close behind, they admired the work going on in the city, and found that the once restful oasis Medina had been transformed into a vibrant city. Everywhere they looked, there was activity: new buildings, new roads, new bridges. Slowly but surely we approached the neighbourhood where Ali, his wife Fatima, and their two little ones, Hassan and Husayn, lived.

I thought Muhammad had intentionally chosen to hold the meeting in Ali's house, away from the commotion of the city. How was I to know he missed his grandsons and wanted to cast an adoring gaze at them before meeting with the merchants.

When we reached Ali's house, Muhammad stopped out front. He dismounted and said to me, 'I'll be right back.'

He headed inside without saying anything to the delegation.

I kept the men occupied by telling them about the changes in the city and the new government buildings. I also told them about the large military barracks being built outside the walls of the city.

Muhammad's absence lasted longer than expected, and I noticed that the delegation began to wonder where he was.

'He's consulting with Ali,' I explained.

We waited a bit longer, yet he did not return. I was worried, knocked on the door, and went inside. What I found there was completely unacceptable, given the fact that the princely merchants of Mecca were waiting for him.

Ali had gone off with his eldest son and left Husayn home with his mother. Husayn was crying because his father had not taken him along too. Muhammad could not bear Husayn's crying. He was so preoccupied with trying to cheer him up, he simply forgot about the entire delegation.

I just stood there, absolutely astounded, looking at Muhammad.

'It's okay, don't cry anymore. Come on, let's go look for your father,' Muhammad said to little Husayn. Muhammad crouched down beside Husayn and said, 'Jump on my back! Then we'll find your father even faster.'

With some difficulty, little Husayn climbed up on Muhammad's back, wobbled, and plunked himself down.

'Are you ready?' Muhammad asked.

Little Husayn grabbed hold of Muhammad's braids as if they were reins and said, 'Yes. Now I won't fall off.'

'Just a minute,' Muhammad said, 'what am I now? A horse? Or a camel?'

'A camel,' Husayn replied, smiling.

Muhammad walked around on his hands and feet imitating the sway of a camel.

88 By the Morning Star

It seemed as if Muhammad's days were coming to a close. When he passed from this world, he had reached the pinnacle of happiness.

Without any warning, he came down with a high fever. And when the fever was gone, it seemed like Muhammad was gone as well. He was no longer his old self. It was as if a candle had been extinguished in the night.

He lost a lot of weight and had trouble standing. The messenger could barely walk. Exhausted, he would have to lean against the wall in the courtyard.

They wanted to carry him to the mosque but he refused, 'I'd rather crawl than be carried.'

Leaning up against walls, he stumbled to the mosque.

Aisha watched from behind the curtain and wept quietly.

Abu Bakr was in Mecca, he was in charge of the city. Umar, Uthman, and Ali were constantly on the road to enforce the new legal system.

There was nobody around to lead the daily prayers in the mosque.

One day Muhammad said to me, 'Zayd! I'm not strong enough to leave my bed today, but people are waiting for me in the mosque. You must lead the prayers!'

I immediately washed my hands, feet, and face, put on clean clothes, belted Muhammad's sword to my side, saddled my horse, and rode to the mosque. I turned to face Mecca and led the prayers, much to everyone's sorrow.

From that moment on, Muhammad no longer went to the mosque.

He lay in bed all day, and I read to him from a book that a courier had delivered. It was a Greek code of law that had been especially translated for Muhammad.

At a certain moment, he said, 'Stop, it's enough. Read me something from the Qur'an!'

I searched my memory for a beautiful text, and while Muhammad listened with his eyes closed, I recited this sura:

> 'We opened the gates of heaven and caused water to fall.
> Obey Allah and obey His prophet.
> And We caused the earth to split apart so that springs started to flow.
> Obey Allah and obey His prophet.
> Oh, people! Go in search of His favours and you shall meet God.'

Muhammad just lay there without moving. Tears trickled into his grey beard. I realized that reciting the Qur'an was the best medicine for him. I read him another text:

> 'By the sky and the night star.
> How do you know which star is the night star?
> It is a radiant star.
> Humankind should be aware of what they are made.
> They are made of leaping fluid that runs from the back of the father to the ribs of the mother.
> Indeed, He is able to call back humankind.

On the day that the secrets are revealed.
By the heavens from which the rain falls.
The Qur'an is a recitation, conclusive in all respects.'

89 Imminent Death

Muhammad could no longer leave the house.

His daughter Fatima visited him almost every day with her sons. It was the only distraction Muhammad had. He always surprised them with special treats. Mecca's merchants knew how to make Muhammad happy. They brought back sweets from faraway countries for his grandchildren. I, Zayd, hid these treats everywhere in his room, in the courtyard, under the date trees, and in between the bushes. His grandsons had to search for the sweets and then show them to Muhammad. I wonder if he ever enjoyed anything more than those candy hunts.

Abu Bakr, Umar, Uthman, and Ali were back in Medina, but Muhammad's physician would not allow them to visit too often because then Muhammad always wanted to know about everything going on in the country. Only Abu Bakr was permitted to give him a general update about the situation.

'Zayd, I want to go lie in Aisha's room,' Muhammad said one night.

I did not want to acknowledge it, but I thought to myself, Muhammad is ready to depart this life.

I immediately let Aisha know that Muhammad wanted to be with her.

The young Aisha was shaken by the idea of Muhammad's imminent death, but she was more than happy that Muhammad wanted to die in her bed. She wept with joy and sadness, and her hands trembled as she readied her bed for him.

Together we helped him to his feet. He heaved one arm over my shoulder and the other over Aisha's shoulder. That is how we took him to Aisha's bed.

Aisha watched over him like a tigress. She let nobody else into her room. Especially none of Muhammad's other wives. Even his daughter Fatima was not allowed to see him anymore.

I remember Aisha's words:

'The messenger has chosen to be with me.

So the messenger is now mine.

The messenger has found peace at my side.

Stay away from my room.

His mission is done. There will be no new revelations.

The Qur'an is complete.'

Aisha's father, Abu Bakr, wanted to visit Muhammad, but she also stopped him, 'Father! His mission is done. Let him be! He's no longer the messenger.'

Abu Bakr pushed her aside and went into the room. Aisha burst into tears, 'Father, why won't you listen? My husband is sleeping.'

I, Zayd, was the only one allowed near her room, and I followed her orders.

'Zayd, I need to rest for a little while. Watch over him?'

I guarded the door to her room and watched over him.

One day, she cried out, 'Zayd! The fever is back. He's burning up! Zayd, go fetch Muhammad's physician!'

I went into the room, felt Muhammad's forehead. He was burning up and unconscious.

'Shall I warn Abu Bakr?'

‘Yes, get my father,’ she answered with tears running down her cheeks.

I also rode to Umar, Uthman, and Ali, and informed them.

They all came. We could tell from the physician’s expression that the messenger had embarked on his final journey.

On Abu Bakr’s command, I placed a large copper tub in the room, one normally used for bathing. Abu Bakr undressed Muhammad. Ali and Umar carefully lifted him into the tub. Uthman gently poured water over him to lower the fever, and Aisha looked on, still weeping.

I carried seven buckets of water inside. They poured all seven buckets over his head until the fever subsided. Aisha immediately dried him and wrapped a blanket around his shoulders, and the men helped him back into bed.

‘Now I want everyone to go home,’ Aisha said.

Abu Bakr told her to calm down.

‘Everybody get out!’ Aisha shouted.

‘Aisha! Control yourself!’ Abu Bakr scolded her.

‘My husband is sleeping. Everyone get out of my room!’

Nobody dared say another word. They all left the room.

Aisha was alone with the messenger.

And I, Zayd, stood guard at the door.

90 He Regulates All Things

Years later, Aisha became a powerful woman, perhaps the most powerful woman in the world. She rode on an elephant. I went looking for her, so I could accurately describe the last phase of Muhammad's life.

I went to her palace seven times to arrange an appointment, but in vain. I was stopped at the door.

I was patient. I went by many times, until I ran into her once in front of her palace, as she was being helped down from her elephant, and I shouted, 'Aisha!'

She was wearing a transparent green veil over her face. She looked around.

'It's me, Zayd. I'm writing about Muhammad. I'd like to ask you a few things.'

She turned and walked inside. I thought she did not want to speak to me. Yet, a moment later, a servant appeared and said, 'My lady is willing to see you. Follow me.'

Escorted by three bodyguards, I entered her home.

I do not know how the Persian queens once lived, and in our long history we had never had an Arabian queen, but Aisha certainly met my expectations of how a queen should live.

Surrounded by beautiful, young servants, she was perched on a golden throne, leaning on silk cushions adorned with precious gems. The room was lit by large candles in silver candleholders.

She had put on weight and there was nothing of that mischievous young Aisha left. I had also changed, and perhaps that is why she scrutinized me in silence for a moment.

'Everything has changed, Zayd,' she said.

'Everything,' I agreed.

'Have a seat, Zayd.'

'I was offered a red satin chair embroidered with flowers.

'Tell me, Zayd, what do you need to know from me?'

'Would you tell me what happened that night when you sent everyone away and stayed alone with the messenger in your room?'

Aisha was silent; she did not want to talk about it.

To convince her of the importance of her story I said, 'You're not only the queen of the realm. This has to be part of history. My book is not meant for people living today, but for those who will live a thousand years from now.'

'Zayd, can you believe it? My husband Muhammad is dead; my father Abu Bakr is dead. Umar, Uthman, and Ali: the three of them murdered—it feels like it all happened in a single moment. It seems like only yesterday that you all doused Muhammad in cold water to lower his fever.

'Once everyone was gone, I locked the door. I dabbed his forehead with a cloth and dressed him in his long white jellaba.

'I dimmed the light of the lantern, crawled under the blanket, lay against him, put my head on his chest, and closed my eyes. I wanted to hold on to that moment for all eternity. If he didn't want to open his eyes, I didn't want to open my eyes either. And if he died, I also wanted to die. I don't know how long it took, but at one point I sat up, and in the dim light I saw that he was looking at me and smiling. I was filled with happiness and kissed his head, his eyes, his nose, and his mouth.

He said something, so softly I couldn't understand it. I put my ear to his mouth, he repeated it, but I still couldn't understand. Then he closed his eyes and was gone.

'I was still young; I had never experienced death from close by. I calmly left my bed, covered his face with my green veil, tiptoed away and walked barefoot to my father's house. I felt like I was sleepwalking. The guard escorted me into the courtyard. My father appeared on the porch. He knew right away, but still he asked, "Aisha! Why are you here?"

"The messenger is no more," I said and collapsed on the ground.'

I, Zayd, was outside her door when Aisha left. I let her go, and went into the room where Muhammad was lying. I picked up the lantern and looked at his face, which was covered with her green veil.

I knelt beside him and recited a sura:

> *'Alif Lam Mim Ra'*
>
> 'The forerunners shall be brought to the gardens of happiness, where they shall sit opposite one another on couches encrusted with jewels.
>
> Young men who never age shall go around with jugs and cups of wine drawn from a flowing spring.
>
> This wine shall not pain their heads or intoxicate them.
>
> And fruit shall be brought, from which they are free to choose what they desire.
>
> And the flesh of birds, whatever their desire.
>
> And wholesome maidens with beautiful, dark, and expressive eyes like well-preserved pearls.
>
> As reward for their good deeds.'

Then the door opened. Abu Bakr, Umar, Uthman, and Ali entered the room. I stood up and lifted the lantern. The four of them knelt around Muhammad's bed and Abu Bakr softly recited:

"Alif Mim Ra'
He regulates the world.
By the earth, and He who made it so vast.
He set the mountains in motion.
He caused water to flow.
He made the heavens with invisible pillars.
He tamed the sun and the moon.
They each move in their own orbit across the vault of heaven.
He regulates the affairs of the universe.
He covers the night with the day, and He covers the day with the night.'

Then they went and sat on the floor some distance from the messenger. Muhammad's successor needed be chosen right away. And they had to hurry, because the decision had to be made before sunrise.

But it didn't take long. Umar, Uthman, and Ali all called out Abu Bakr's name at the same time. That's how Abu Bakr became the first Caliph.

They rose and kissed Abu Bakr on his left shoulder.

The messenger was dead. The first Caliph had been chosen.

They rode on their four horses to the mosque, and I followed closely behind on my horse.

The town crier called the people to the mosque.

Umar announced, 'The Caliph Abu Bakr will lead the prayers!'

Abu Bakr belted Muhammad's sword to his waist and turned to face Mecca.

It was now clear to everyone that Muhammad was gone.

91 Parting Words

The story of the messenger that I wanted to share with the world is far from over, but I must stop now. That is the law of storytelling—at some point, tales come to an end.

By the time you read this, I shall be long gone.

I, Zayd, shall rest peacefully in my grave if I have fulfilled my task well.

Muhammad did it for Him.

I did it for Muhammad.

Zayd ibn Thalith
The Chronicler of Muhammad ibn Abdullah
7th day, month of Shawwal, year 40
Mecca

Translator's Note:

Most of the English sura fragments in this book have been borrowed from or reflect the suras in Kader Abdolah's *The Qur'an*, which was originally published in Dutch (2008) together with *The Messenger*. Other sura fragments in the story are inspired by Tarif Khalidi's *Qur'an, A New Translation*, © 2008, Penguin Books Ltd., London.

The Bible verses Zayd quotes in *The Messenger* (p. 49 and p. 158-159) are based on the *New Revised Standard Version Bible* (www.biblestudytools.com), © 1989, Division of Christian Education of the National Council of the Churches of Christ in the United States of America. Used by permission. All rights reserved.

I would like to express my thanks to Kader Abdolah, Nadia, and Jetske for answering my many questions about the text, the Arabic language, and Islam. Additionally, my sincere thanks to Nouri for sharing his words. And last but not least, my loving thanks to IHO for always holding my hand.

Salaam!

NIUSHA NIGHTING

'These books will build a bridge between East and West.'
—*Kader Abdolah* on *The Qur'an* and *The Messenger*

With his translation, now available in English, Kader Abdolah has made the Qur'an accessible for both Muslims and non-Muslims. He has not tried to write a polemic, nor is it his aim to seek out controversy. More than anything he wants to facilitate a dialogue and contribute to creating a positive image of Islam. And he has done so successfully. The social discussion created by the release of this book in the Netherlands was widely applauded by politicians and lawmakers. Reactions from the Dutch Islamic community were positive as well. The publication made the front page of Dutch newspapers, and the book was also regularly discussed on prime-time TV shows.

'It is sensational work. Daring, loving and beautiful.'
—*Director of Oxfam-Novib, Farah Karimi*